Name Th

Gerard Kelly

NAME THAT SONG

The Great Pop Music Lyrics Quiz Book

Matador
9 De Montfort Mews
Leicester LE1 7FW, UK
Tel: (+44) 116 255 9311 / 9312
Email: books@troubador.co.uk
Web: www.troubador.co.uk/matador

ISBN 1 904744 72 9

Cover illustration: © Photos.com

Typeset in 10pt Univers by Troubador Publishing Ltd, Leicester, UK
Printed by The Cromwell Press Ltd, Trowbridge, Wilts, UK

Matador is an imprint of Troubador Publishing

NAME THAT SONG

is a music quiz with a difference...

Over 1000 carefully compiled snippets from well-known songs.

Your challenge is to name the song title and artist.

EXAMPLE

For forty days and forty nights
The law was on her side

Now what big hit song is that from?

(Answer at the bottom of this page)

All the songs have been major chart hits, and in most instances have stood the test of time. There are no obscure songs, but it is sometimes harder than it appears to recall the exact song title or the artist. Some will tease and frustrate as you silently 'sing' the words and 'hum' the tune in an effort to reach the answer – some songs may even appear more than once.

To make it more challenging for all skill levels, there are levels of difficulty – some questions have up to four lines, making them relatively easy, some have just one line and pose a more difficult challenge.

There are also selections by specific artists, one hit wonders and hits from musicals.

Enjoy!

Billy Jean – Michael Jackson

CONTENTS

Nice 'n' Easy from A to Z

1. And just because
    I call you up
    Don't get me wrong, don't think you've got it made

2. Come on, come on, love me for the money
    Come on, come on, listen to the moneytalk

3. Playing in a rocking band
    Hey Momma, look at me
    I'm on my way to the promised land

4. I take—2 steps forward
    I take—2 steps back
    We come together
    Cuz......

5. Me and some guys from school
    Had a band and we tried real hard
    Jimmy quit and Jody got married
    I shoulda known we'd never get far

6. Don't tell me it's not worth tryin' for
    You can't tell me it's not worth dyin' for

7. I know, you know, I just want us to go
    The fun we'll have fun you'll never be alone
    So boy, won't you come?
    We will party till the dawn. Listen to me...

8.   While I figured it out I only looked,
        but I never touched
      'Cause in my heart was a picture of us
      Holding hands, making plans
      And lucky for me, you understand

9.   Every day is so wonderful
      And suddenly, it's hard to breathe
      Now and then, I get insecure
      From all the fame, I'm so ashamed

10. Talking away
      I don't know what I'm to say
      I'll say it anyway
      Today's another day to find you
      Shying away

11. After two days in the desert sun
      My skin began to turn red
      After three days in the desert fun
      I was lookin' at a river bed

12. Life in plastic, it's fantastic!
      You can brush my hair, undress me everywhere
      Imagination, life is your creation

13. I see trees of green, red roses too
      I see 'em bloom for me and you

14. If you were me, what would you do
      Always a lie and never the truth
      Now as for me, I'm movin' on
      You'll always be my baby

15. We're no strangers to love
     You know the rules and so do I
     A full commitment's what I'm thinking of
     You wouldn't get this from any other guy

16. So don't stop me falling
     It's destiny calling
     A power I just can't deny
     It's never changing

17. She may be the song that Solomon sings
     May be the chill that autumn brings
     May be a hounded tearful things
     Within the measure of the day.

18. I got me a car, it's as big as a whale
     And we're headin' on down
     To the......

19. My mother was a tailor
     She sewed my new blue jeans
     My father was a gamblin' man

20. Friday night and the lights are low
     Looking out for the place to go

21. I met a devil woman.
     She took my heart away.
     She said I had it coming to me.
     I wanted it that way.

22. Tell me why
     Ain't nothin' but a heartache –
     Tell me why

Ain't nothin' but a mistake
Tell me why
I never wanna hear you say

23. Virgil Caine is the name and I served on the
Danville train
Till Stoneman's Cavalry came an´ tore up the
tracks again

24. Last year in the dance you had a ball
You call me millibug and skettell
Get back gruffy, mash scruffy
Get back you flea infested mongrel

25. Goddess on the mountain top
Burning like a silver flame
The summit of beauty and love

26. You've been around all night and that's a
little long
You think you've got the right but I think
you've got it wrong
Why can't you say goodnight so you can take
me home,

27. They are all I need to please me,
They can stimulate and tease me,
They won't leave in the night,
I've no fear that they might desert me.

28. Well since she put me down I 've been out doin'
in my head
I come in late at night and in the mornin' I just
lay in bed

29. I love the colorful clothes she wears
    And the way the sunlight plays upon her hair
    I hear the sound of a gentle word
    On the wind that lifts her perfume through the air

30. Give me just a second and I'll be all right
    Surely one more moment couldn't break my heart
    Give me 'til tomorrow then I'll be okay
    Just another day and then I'll hold you tight

31. Tried to hitch a ride to San Francisco
    Gotta do the things I wanna do

32. Here I lie
    In a lost and lonely part of town
    Held in time
    In a world of tears I slowly drown
    Goin' home

33. Trumpets sound and angels sing,
    Listen to what they say,
    The glory that was Rome is of another day
    I've been terribly alone and forgotten in Manhattan
    I'm going home to my city by the Bay

34. Turning and returning
    To some secret place inside
    Watching in slow motion
    As you turn around and say

35. Ridin' along in my automobile
    I'm anxious to tell her the way I feel,
    So I told her softly and sincere,
    And she leaned and whispered in my ear

5

36. You know, my temperature's risin'
And the jukebox blows a fuse
My heart's beatin' rhythm
And my soul keeps on singin' the blues

37. Here I stand, watching the tide go out
So all alone and blue
Just dreaming dreams of you

38. Until the rainbow burns the stars out of the sky
Until the ocean covers every mountain high
Until the day that eight times eight times eight
 is four
Until the day that it's the day that I'm no more

39. In between, what I find is pleasing
And I'm feeling fine, love is so confusing
There's no peace of mind

40. I'm not the kind of girl
Who gives up just like that
Oh, no

(*Spoken*)
41. We're so glad to see so many of you lovely people
here tonight and we would especially like to
welcome all the representatives of Illinois law
enforcement community who have chosen to join
us here in The Palace Hotel Ballroom at this time.
We do sincerely hope you all enjoy the show.

42. If she is bad, he can't see it
She can do no wrong
Turn his back on his best friend
If he puts her down

6

43. I ain't got a fever got a permanent disease
     It'll take more than a doctor to prescribe
      a remedy
     I got lots of money but it isn't what I need

44. She says: We've got to hold on to what we've got
     'Cause it doesn't make a difference
     If we make it or not

45. Yeah, I'm a wanted man
     I'm a colt in your stable
     I'm what Cain was to Abel
     Mister catch me if you can

46. I heard a rumour from ground control
     Oh no, don't say it's true
     They got a message from the action man
     I'm happy hope you're happy too

47. If you say run, I'll run with you
     If you say hide, we'll hide
     Because my love for you
     Would break my heart in two

48. Didn't know what time it was and the lights
      were low
     I leaned back on my radio
     Some cat was layin
     Down some Rock 'n' Roll,

49. And I know you're shining down on me
      from Heaven
     Like so many friends we've lost along the way
     And I know eventually we'll be together

50. I think it's time we got this straight
    Let's sit and talk face to face
    There is no way you could mistake him for
      your man
    Are you insane?

51. Undo this hurt you caused
    When you walked out the door
    And walked outta my life
    Un-cry these tears
    I cried so many nights

52. Maybe I'm a crazy
    But I just can't live without
    Your love and affection
    Givin' me direction

53. He can make you love, he can make you cry
    He will bring you down, then he'll get you high
    Somethin' keeps him goin', miles and miles a day
    To find another place to play.

54. And now I'm glad I didn't know
    The way it all would end the way it all would go
    Our lives are better left to chance I could
      have missed the pain

55. Sometimes late at night
    I lie awake and watch her sleeping
    She's lost in peaceful dreams
    So I turn out the lights and lay there in the dark

56. Super highways, coast to coast,
    Easy to get anywhere
    On the transcontinental overload,
    Just slide behind the wheel
    How does it feel?

57. Now the promoter don't mind
    And the union don't mind
    If we take a little time
    And we leave it all behind and sing

58. I hated you, I loved you too
    Bad dreams in the night
    They told me I was going to lose the fight

59. They took the credit for your second symphony.
    Rewritten by machine and new technology,
    And now I understand the problems you can see.

60. Take me for a trip
    Upon your magic swirling ship
    All my senses have been stripped
    And my hands can't feel to grip

61. And I dream of the things I'll do
    With a subway token and a dollar tucked inside
      my shoe

62. Baby look at me
    And tell me what you see.
    You ain't seen the best of me yet
    Give me time, I'll make you forget the rest

63. All alone I have cried silent tears full of pride
    In a world made of steel, made of stone

64. Ooh, baby, do you know what that's worth?
    Ooh heaven is a place on earth
    They say in heaven love comes first

65. No I can't forget this evening
    Or your face as you were leaving
    But I guess that's just the way
    The story goes

66. Who's gonna pick you up,
    When you fall?
    Who's gonna hang it up,
    When you call?

67. You're always dancing down the street
    With your suede blue eyes
    And every new boy that you meet
    He doesn't know the real surprise

68. Well, it was Gatlinburg in mid-July
    And I just hit town and my throat was dry,
    I thought I'd stop and have myself a brew.

69. The taste of love is sweet
    When hearts like ours meet
    I fell for you like a child
    Oh, but the fire went wild

70. Nothing in the world could bother me
    'Cos I was living in a world of ecstasy.
    But now you're gone I'm just....

71. I am a man who will fight for your honor
    I'll be the hero you're dreaming of
    We'll live forever
    Knowing together that we did it all for

72. Playing all the hits for you wherever you may be
    The bright good-morning voice who's heard
     but never seen
    Feeling all of forty-five going on fifteen

73. Maybe together we can get somewhere
     Anyplace is better
     Starting from zero got nothing to lose
     Maybe we'll make something
     But me myself I got nothing to prove

74. Ooh I've been to Georgia and California
     And, anywhere I could run
     I took the hand of a preacher man
     And we made love in the sun

75. Those happy hours that we once knew
     Tho' long ago, they still make me blue
     They say that time heals a broken heart
     But time has stood still since we've been apart

76. Who's that, flyin up there?
     Is it a bird? Noooooo
     Is it a plane? Noooooooo
     Is it the twister? YEAAAAAAAHH!

77. I never ever ask what do you do
     I never ever ask what's in your mind
     I never ever ask if you'll be mine
     Come and smile don't be shy

78. No matter how hard I try
     You keep pushing me aside
     And I can't break through
     There's no talking to you

79. All that pressure got you down
     Has your head spinning all around
     Feel the rhythm, check the ride
     Come on along and have a real good time

80. A love like ours is love that's hard to find
    How could we let it slip away
    We've come too far to leave it all behind
    How could we end it all this way

81. "Everybody needs a little time away," I heard
    her say,
    "From each other."
    "Even lover's need a holiday far away from
    each other."

82. They say they want to bring me in guilty
    For the killing of a deputy
    For the life of a deputy, but I say:

83. Would you know my name
    If I saw you in heaven?
    Would you feel the same
    If I saw you in heaven?

84. We go a party
    And everyone turns to see
    This beautiful lady
    That's walking around with me

85. Just listen to the music of the traffic in the city
    Linger on the sidewalk where the neon signs
    are pretty
    How can you lose?

86. You say that you love me, all of the time
    You say that you need me, and you'll always
    be mine

87. If you say that you are mine
I'll be here 'til the end of time
So you got to let me know

88. Ain't got time to fix his shingles
Ain't got time to fix the door
Ain't got time to oil the hinges
Nor to mingle the window panes

89. Well we'll really have a party but we gotta put
a guard outside
If the folks come home I'm afraid they gonna
have my hide
There'll be no more movies for a week or two
No more runnin' 'round with the usual crew
Who cares

90. What do I do when my love is away
(Does it worry you to be all alone)
How do I feel by the end of the day
(Are you sad because you're on your own)

91. All I know is the way I feel
When it's real I keep it alive
The road is long there are mountains in the way

92. I remember the things that we used to do,
A kiss in the rain til' the sun shined through,
I'd try to deny it, but I'm still in love with you

93. How can I just let you walk away
Just let you leave without a trace?
When I stand here taking every breath with you

13

94. I need love, love
    Ooh, ease my mind
    And I need to find time
    Someone to call mine;

95. I'll never forget the moment we kissed,
    The night of the hayride,
    The way that we hugged to try to keep warm,
    While takin' a sleigh ride.

96. Don't look so sad, I know it's over,
    But life goes on and this ol' world will
        keep on turning.

97. Don't know much about history,
    Don't know much biology.
    Don't know much about a science book,
    Don't know much about the French I took.

98. As I walk through the valley of the shadow
        of death
    I take a look at my life
    And realize there's nothing left

99. I had to let it happen, I had to change
    Couldn't stay all my life down at heel
    Looking out of the window, staying out of the sun

100. You'd better believe I'm coming
     You'd better believe what I say
     You'd better hold on to your promises
     Because you bet you'll get what you deserve.

101. I cannot lie, from you I cannot hide
      And I'm losing the will to try
      Can't hide it (can't hide it),
      can't fight it (can't fight it)

102. Hope you got your things together
      Hope you are quite prepared to die
      Looks like we're in for nasty weather

103. Cleaned a lot of plates in Memphis
      Pumped a lot of pain down in New Orleans
      But I never saw the good side of the city
      Until I hitched a ride on a riverboat queen.

104. He says his name's William but I'm sure
      He's Bill or Billy, Mac or Buddy, he's plain
        ugly to me.
      And I wonder if he's ever had fun in his life.

105. I look and stare so deep in your eyes,
      I touch on you more and more every time,
      When you leave I'm begging you not to go,
      Call your name two or three times in a row,

106. When no one is around you, say baby I love you
      If you ain't runnin' game

107. Her diary it sits on the bedside table
      The curtains are closed, the cats in the cradle
      Who would've thought that a boy like me
        could come to this

108. But if you dig on Vegan food,
      Well come over to my work,
      I'll have them cook you something that
        you'll really love,

109. Hugging like a monkey see
Monkey do
Right beside a riverboat gambler

110. See the tree how big it's grown
But friend it hasn't been too long it wasn't big
I laughed at her and she got mad
The first day that she planted it, it was just a twig

111. I can hear your music playing.
I can feel your body swaying.
One floor below me,
You don't even know me,

112. If you received my letter telling you I'd soon
be free,
Then you'll know just what to do if you still
want me,

113. And I have never seen that dress you're wearing,
Or the highlights in your hair that catch your eyes,
I have been blind;

114. When I was down
I was your clown
Nobody knows it
Right from the start
I gave you my heart

115. On the sidewalk, Sunday morning
Lies a body oozing life
Someone's sneaking round the corner

116. I don't feel so bright,
     I don't care to sit tight.
     Maybe I'll find on the way down the line
     That I'm free, free to be me.

117. Get up in the morning, slaving for bread, sir,
     So that every mouth can be fed.

118. You actin' kinda shady
     Ain't callin me baby
     Why the sudden change?

119. See I'm down and out
     And I ain't about to go
     Living my life without you
     Hey every day, I made you cry
     I'm begging girl, 'til the day I die

120. Poor old Johnny Ray
     Sounded sad upon the radio, he moved a
       million hearts in mono.
     Our mothers cried and sang along and
       who'd blame them.

121. The whispers in the morning
     Of lovers sleeping tight
     Are rolling like thunder now
     As I look in your eyes

122. We gotta install microwave ovens
     Custom kitchen deliveries
     We gotta move these refrigerators
     We gotta move these colour TV's

123. You check out Guitar George, he knows all the chords
Mind he's strictly rhythm he doesn't want to make
   it cry or sing

124. 'Cause everybody wants her, everybody loves her
Everybody wants to take your baby home

125. You made me cry when you said good-bye
Ain't that a shame my tears fall like rain

126. Don't you feel it growin', day by day
People gettin' ready for the news
Some are happy, some are sad
Oh, we got to let the music play

127. You know that it would be untrue
You know that I would be a liar
If I was to say to you
Girl, we couldn't get much higher

128. There was funky Billie Jim
And little Sammy John
He said, here comes the big boss,
Let's get it on

129. You can smile
Ev'y smile for the man
Who hold your hand
'Neath the pale moonlight.

130. My heart is breaking
When I see her holding hands with him
Can't help thinking how it might have been

131. I'm on a ride and I want to get off
     But they won't slow down the roundabout
     I sold the Renoir and the TV set
     Don't want to be around when this gets out

132. Come gather 'round people
     Wherever you roam
     And admit that the waters
     Around you have grown

133. How many years can a mountain exist
     Before it's washed to the sea?
     Yes, 'n' how many years can some people exist
     Before they're allowed to be free?

134. You been down to the bottom with a bad man, babe,
     But you're back where you belong.
     Go get me my pistol, babe,
     Honey, I can't tell right from wrong.

135. I'll tell you once more before I get off the floor

136. From the North to the South, Ebudau unto Khartoum.
     From the deep Sea of Clouds to the Island of the Moon.
     Carry me on the waves to the lands I've never seen.

137. It's not the way you lead me
     By the hand into the bedroom
     It's not the way you leave your clothes
     Upon the bathroom floor

138. Baby when you're loving me
     I feel like I could cry
     'Cause there's nothing I can do
     To keep from loving you

139. I travel the world and the seven seas
Everybody's looking for somethin'.
Some of them want to use you
Some of them want to get used by you

140. There goes my baby with someone new.
She sure looks happy
I sure am blue.

141. Don't want your love anymore
Don't want your kisses, that's for sure
I die each time I hear this sound
Here he comes

142. I don't know what I'd do without you babe
don't know where I'd be
You're not just another lover
no you're everything to me
Every time I'm with you baby can't believe it's true
When your laying in my arms
and you do the things you do

143. Because er hatte Flair
Er war ein Virtuose
War ein Rockidol
Und alles rief:
Come on and rock me

144. I can't stop, The way I feel
Things you do, Don't seem real
Tell you what I got in mind
'Cause we're runnin' out of time

145. And there he was this young boy
A stranger to my eyes
Struming my pain with his fingers

146. Can you hear me calling
Out your name
You know that I'm falling
And I don't know what to say

147. In my life there's been heartache and pain
I don't know if I can face it again
Can't stop now, I've traveled so far
To change this lonely life

148. All my life I've been searching for somethin'
Somethin' never comes, never leads to nuthin'
Nothin' satisfies, but I'm gettin' close
Closer to the prize at the end of the rope

149. And so I wake in the morning
And I step outside
And I take a deep breath and I get real high

150. I got a funny feelin' when she walked in the room
Oh my
As I recall it ended much too soon.

151. Now if you feel that you can't go on
Because all your hope is gone
And your life is filled with confusion
And happiness is just an illusion

152. Scheme those schemes
Got to hit me
Hit me
Hit me with those laser beams

153. And the river was deep I didn't falter
When the mountain was high
I still believed
When the valley was low
It didn't stop me

154. Did you see Lisa? Yes I saw Lisa.
Is that why...You're.. Angry?
I wasn't angry.
Maybe a little. Not even maybe.

155. You could have a steam train
If you'd just lay down your tracks
You could have an aeroplane flying
If you bring your blue sky back

156. There's a fog along the horizon,
A strange glow in the sky,
And nobody seems to know where you go,
And what does it mean?

157. I bet you wonderin' how I knew
'Bout your planes to make me blue
With some other guy you knew before
Between two of us guys you know I love you more

158. Go on now go walk out the door
Just turn around now
'Cause you're not welcome anymore

159. She was pure like snowflakes, no one could ever stain
The memory of my angel could never cause me pain
Years go by, I'm looking through a girlie magazine
And there's my homeroom angel on the pages
in between

160. If you should go, go, go, go, go, go,
    If you should go, go, go, go, go, go,
    If you should go, go, go, go, go, go,
    If you should go, go, go, go, go, go.

161. I talked to my baby on the telephone, long distance.
    I never knew anyone could miss someone so bad.
    I really only met her 'bout a week ago, but
    It doesn't really matter to my heart, I know that;

162. Down in the street there is violence
    And a lots of work to be done
    No place to hang out our washing
    And I can't blame all on the sun, oh no

163. Mama put my guns in the ground
    I can't shoot them anymore
    That cold black cloud is comin' down

164. Baby, I'm an addict now
    An addict for your love
    I was a stray boy
    And you was my best toy

165. She'll only come out at night
    The lean and hungry type
    Nothing is new, I've seen her here before
    Watching and waiting

166. Thank you for blessing me with a mind to rhyme
      and to hype beat
    That's good when you know you're down
    A superbowl homeboy from Oaktown
    And I'm known as such

167. My happiness was paid for when they laid their
money down
For summers in a summer camp and winters
in the town
My future in the system was talked about and planned

168. Someone left the cake out in the rain
I don't think that I can take it
'Cause it took so long to bake it
And I'll never have that recipe again
Oh, no!

169. I really want to know you
Really want to go with you
Really want to show you lord
That it won't take long, my lord

170. But it's gonna take money
A whole lotta spending money
It's gonne take plenty of money
To do it right child

171. Lately things just don't seem the same
Actin' funny I don't know why
'Scuse me while I kiss the sky

172. The road is long
With many a winding turn
That leads us to who knows where
Who knows where

173. Take the ribbon from your hair
Shake it loose, let it fall
Lay it soft against my skin
Like the shadow on the wall

174. Aaah baby, my heart is full of love and desire for you
Now come on down and do what you gotta do
(Now come on girl and do what you gotta do)

175. If I should stay,
I would only be in your way.
So I'll go
But I know
I'll think of you every step of the way.

176. There's a boy I know, he's the one I dream of
Looks into my eyes, takes me to the clouds above
Ooh I lose control, can't seem to get enough
When I wake from dreaming, tell me is it really love

177. Our love is like a ship on the ocean
We've been sailing with a cargo full of,
 love and devotion

178. Now five years later on you've got the world at your feet
Success has been so easy for you.
But don't forget it's me who put you where you are now
And I can put you back down too.

179. She was afraid to come out of the locker
She was as nervous as she could be
She was afraid to come out of the locker
She was afraid that somebody would see

180. Hey little sister what have you done
Hey little sister who's the only one
Hey little sister who's your superman
Hey little sister who's the one you want
Hey little sister shot gun!

181. Goodbye to you my trusted friend
     We've known each other since we were nine or ten
     Together we've climbed hills and trees
     Learned of love and abc's

182. Everywhere I go
     Every smile I see
     I know you are there
     Smilin' back at me

183. Annie are you ok
     So, Annie are you ok
     Are you ok, Annie

184. It's too high to get over (yeah, yeah)
     Too low to get under (yeah, yeah)
     You're stuck in the middle (yeah, yeah)
     And the pain is thunder (yeah, yeah)

185. He rocks in the treetops all day long
     Hoppin' and a-boppin' and a-singin' his song
     All the little birdies on J-Bird Street

186. Better stop dreaming of the quiet life -
     Cos it's the one we'll never know
     And quit running for that runaway bus -
     Cos those rosey days are few

187. But that's the way that you are
     And that's the things that you say
     But now you've gone too far
     With all the things you say

188. I saw him dancing there by the record machine
I knew he must have been about seventeen
The beat was going strong, playing my favorite song
And I could tell it wouldn't be long

189. Joe McCarthy, Richard Nixon, Studebaker, Television
North Korea, South Korea, Marilyn Monroe
Rosenbergs, H bomb, Sugar Ray, Panmunjom
Brando, The King And I, and The Catcher In The Rye

190. I can't light no more of your darkness
All my pictures seem to fade to black and white
I'm growing tired and time stands still before me
Frozen here on the ladder of my life

191. She packed my bags last night pre-flight
Zero hour nine a.m.
And I'm gonna be high as a kite by then
I miss the earth so much I miss my wife

192. Well they're packed pretty tight in here tonight
I'm looking for a dolly who'll see me right
I may use a little muscle to get what I need
I may sink a little drink and shout out "She's with me!"

193. Driving down those city streets,
Waiting to get down,
Won't you take your big machine,
Somewhere in this town?

194. When we're all all alone,
When you whisper sweet in my ear,
When you turn, turn me on,
Oh, that's the way, uh-huh uh-huh,

195. I used to think maybe you love me, now baby I'm sure
And I just can't wait till the day when you knock
on my door
Now everytime I go for the mailbox gotta hold
myself down
Cause I just can't wait till you write me you're
comin' around

196. I'll be your cloud up in the sky
I'll be your shoulder when you cry
I hear your voices when you call me

197. Chaka khan
Chaka khan.
Chaka khan
Let me love you
Let me rock you

198. I was a sailor I was lost at sea
I was under the waves before love rescued me.
I was a fighter I could turn on a thread
But I stand accused of the things I've said.

199. Touching you so warm and tender
Lord I feel such a sweet surrender
Beautiful is the dream that makes you mine.

200. When the night has come
And the land is dark
And the moon is the only light we see

201. Save me, save me, save me from this squeeze.
I gotta big fat mama trying to break me.
And I love to live so pleasantly,
Live this life of luxury,

202. When you make my motor run, my motor run
     Gun it coming, off the line

203. He said he's goin' back to find
     Ooh, what's left of his world,
     The world he left behind
     Not so long ago.
     He's leaving,

204. It's time to come together
     It's up to you watch your pleasure
     Everyone around the world
     Come on

205. Animal attraction burnin' through the crowd
     Heaven on earth, paradise for a price
     It's cool though, I'll play ya
     For the rest of my life, you know why

206. They sold me a dream of Christmas
     They sold me a Silent Night
     And they told me a fairy story
     'Till I believed in the Israelite

207. When I was born in my birth suit the doctor
       slap her behind
     He said: You're gonna be special
     You sweet little.......

208. Mira lo que se avecina
     A la vuelta de la esquina
     Viene Diego rumbeando.
     Con la luna en las pupilas

209. In a world full of people
You can lose sight of it all
And the darkness inside you
Can make you feel so small

210. You may say I'm a dreamer
But I'm not the only one
I hope someday you'll join us
And the world will be as one

211. My mixed emotions at my thoughtlessness
After all I'm forever in your debt

212. You pull my fingers and you twiddle my thumbs
Wanna love you but a true love huh
Come on baby, your drive me crazy

213. You don't need money, don't take fame
Don't need no credit card to ride this train
It's strong and it's sudden and it's cruel sometimes
But it might just save your life

214. Gotta make a move to a
Town that's right for me
Town to keep me movin'
Keep me groovin' with some energy

215. From the early early morning
Till the early early night
Molly's gonna rocking at the house of blue lights

216. I remember to this day the bright red Georgia clay,
How it stuck to the tires after the summer rain.
Will power made that old car go; a woman's mind
    told me that it's so.
Oh, how I wish we were back on the road again.

217. Kick off your Sunday shoes
Please, Louise
Pull me offa my knees
Jack, get back
C'mon before we crack

218. Used to have a little, now I have a lot
No matter where I go, I know where I came from
    (from the Bronx!)

219. Yo no soy marinero
Yo no soy marinero, por ti sere,
Por ti sere, por ti sere.

220. They all want me, they can't have me
So they all come and dance beside me
Move with me jam with me
And if you're good I take you home with me

221. Well I heard mister Young sing about her
Well, I heard ole Neil put her down
Well, I hope Neil Young will remember
A Southern man don't need him around anyhow

222. Boogie with a suitcase
Your livin' in a disco
Forget about the rat race
Let's do the milkshake,

223. Well, the undertaker drew a heavy sigh
Seeing no one else had come,
And a bell was ringing in the village square
For the rabbits on the run.

224. We all know
That people are the same where ever you go
There is good and bad in ev'ryone,

225. Any time, any day
You can hear the people say,
That love is blind, well, I don't know
But I say love is kind

226. Oh honey, boy, I don't need no superstar cause
I'll accept you as you are
You won't be denied cause I'm satisfied
With the love that you can inspire.

227. I want to encourage everyone
To coordinate your steps and clap
Avoid the individuality trap
Take a walk on the wild side
And the African-American women sing

228. There's nothin' to it just say you wanna do it
Open up your heart and let the lovin' start
Woman, take me in your arms

229. There've been so many things that have held us down
But now it looks like things are finally comin'
   around, yeah
I know we've got a long long way to go, yeah
And where we'll end up I don't know

230. Here is a little song I wrote
     You might want to sing it note for note

231. There you go
     Flashing fever
     From your eyes
     Hey baby, come over here and shut them tight
     I'm not denyin'
     We're flying above it all

232. All across the nation
     Such a strange vibration
     People in motion

233. They would not listen, they did not know how
     Perhaps they'll listen now

234. Every other day, every other day,
     Every other day of the week is fine, yeah

235. She looked good (looked good)
     She looked fine (looked fine)
     She looked good, she looked fine
     And I nearly lost my mind

236. Mornin', just another day
     Happy people pass my way
     Lookin' in their eyes
     I see a memory
     I never realized

237. And while she tried to be a star, Tony always tended bar
Across a crowded floor, they worked from 8 till 4
They were young and they had each other
Who could ask for more?

238. And he was taken from Africa, brought to America,
Fighting on arrival, fighting for survival.

239. Said – said – said: I remember when we used to sit
In the government yard in Trenchtown,
Oba – obaserving the 'ypocrites
As they would mingle with the good people we meet.

240. Just give me the strength to do every day what
    I have to do
Yesterday's gone sweet Jesus
Tomorrow may never be mine

241. Take one fresh and tender kiss
Add one stolen night of bliss
One girl, one boy
Some grief, some joy

242. When the moon hits your eye like a big-a pizza pie

243. She's into superstitions
Black cats and voodoo dolls
I feel a premonition
That girl's gonna make me fall

244. Through early morning fog I see
Visions of the things to be
The pains that are withheld for me
I realize and I can see...

245. There's evil in the air and there's thunder in the sky,
And a killer's on the bloodshot streets.
And down in the tunnels where the deadly are rising
Oh, I swear I saw a young boy down in the gutter
He was starting to foam in the heat.

246. And maybe you can cry all night
But that'll never change the way I feel
The snow is really piling up outside
I wish you wouldn't make me leave here

247. Buying bread from a man in Brussels
He was six foot four and full of muscles
I said, "Do you speak-a my language?"

248. I can pretend each time I see you
That I don't care and I don't need you
And though you'll never see me cryin'
You know inside I feel like dying

249. Should've known better than to cheat a friend
And waste the chance that I've been given
So I'm never gonna dance again
The way I danced with you

250. And when that love comes down
Without devotion
Well it takes a strong man baby
But I'm showing you the door

251. Did you ever know that you're my hero,
And everything I would like to be?
I can fly higher than an eagle,

252. Every generation
    Blames the one before
    And all of their frustrations
    Come beating on your door

253. Music was my first love
    And it will be my last.
    Music of the future
    And music of the past.

254. You got me spinnin'
    'Round and 'round
    'Round and 'round and 'round it goes
    Where it stops nobody knows

255. Cause I'm a picker
    I'm a grinner
    I'm a lover
    And I'm a sinner

256. Won't you stay
    Won't you stay
    Stay forever and ever and ever ah ah

257. Don't it always seem to go
    That you don't know what you got till it's gone
    They paved paradise and put up a parkin' lot

258. But don't let my glad expression
    Give you the wrong impression.
    Really I'm sad.
    I'm sadder than sad.
    You're gone and I'm hurtin' so bad.

259. Oh, I could hide 'neath the wings
     Of the bluebird as she sings.
     The six o'clock alarm would never ring.
     But it rings and I rise,
     Wipe the sleep out of my eyes.
     My shavin' razor's cold and it stings.

260. What's the use in tryin'?
     All you get is pain.
     When I needed sunshine I got rain.

261. Gazing at people,
     Some hand in hand,
     Just what I'm going thru
     They can understand.

262. I only knew you for a while
     I never saw your smile
     Till it was time to go
     Time to go away (time to go away)

263. Why do we always come here
     I guess we'll never know
     It's like a kind of torture
     To have to watch the show

264. Mississippi in the middle of a dry spell
     Jimmy Rogers on the Victrola up high
     Mama's dancin', there's a baby on her shoulder
     The sun is settin' like molasses in the sky

265. I think I can make it now, the pain is gone
     All of the bad feelings have disappeared
     Here is the rainbow I've been prayin' for

266. No matter what I do, all I think about is you
     Even when I'm with my boo, boy you know
        I'm crazy over you
     No matter what I do, all I think about is you
     Even when I'm with my boo, boy you know
        I'm crazy over you'

267. Maybe I didn't treat you
     Quite as good as I should have
     Maybe I didn't love you

268. Hey girl in your eyes
     I see a picture of me all the time
     And girl when you smile
     You got to know that you drive me wild

269. Tell me more, tell me more,
     Did you get very far?
     Tell me more, tell me more,
     Like, does he have a car?

270. Never made it as a wise man
     I couldn't cut it as a poor man stealin
     Tired of livin like a blind man
     I'm sick of sight without a sense of feelin

271. No, I can't forget tomorrow
     When I think of all my sorrows
     When I had you there but then I let you go
     And now it's only fair that I should let you know
     What you should know

272. I don't know what, they want from me
     It's like the more money we come across
     The more problems we see

273. It's cold outside
And the paint's peeling off of my walls
There's a man outside
In a long coat, grey hat, smoking a cigarette

274. I got something to tell you
I got something to say
I'm gonna put this dream in motion
Never let nothing stand in my way

275. It's been so lonely without U here
Like a bird without a song
Nothing can stop these lonely tears from falling
Tell me baby where did I go wrong?

276. The next stop that we make will be soon
Tell all the folks in Russia, and China, too
Don't you know that it's time to get on board
And let this train keep on riding, riding on through

277. Every step I take, every move I make
Every single day, every time I pray
I'll be missing you
Thinkin of the day, when you went away
What a life to take, what a bond to break
I'll be missing you

278. There'll be tomorrow nigh, but wait
What do I see
Is she walking back to me
Yeah, she's walking back to me

279. If Joan of Arc
     Had a heart
     Would she give it as a gift
     To such as me
     Who longs to see
     How an angel ought to be

280. You ask how much I need you
     Must I explain
     I need you, oh my darlin'
     Like roses need rain

281. Don't love me for fun, girl
     Let me be the one, girl

282. But try as hard as I might do, I don't know why.
     You get to me in a way I can't describe.
     Words mean so little when you look up and smile.
     I don't care what people say, to me you're more
       than a child

283. She is D delirious
     She is I incredible
     She is S superficial
     She is C complicated
     She is O oh, oh, oh

284. What can I do to get closer to you?
     Don't think twice or count to ten.
     Don't take advice, don't ask me when.
     Just come my way, simply kiss me and say:

285. I don't want a bunny or a kitty
I don't want a parrot that talks
I don't want a bowl of little fishies
He can't take a goldfish for a walk

286. Your lights are on, but you're not home
Your mind is not your own
Your heart sweats, your body shakes
Another kiss is what it takes

287. Brother what a night it really was
Brother what a fight it really was
Glory be!
I heard my mama cry

288. I can hear the music playin, I can see the banners fly
Feels like you're back again and hope riding high
Gonna be your man in motion, all I need's a pair
    of wheels

289. Baby, when I met you there was peace unknown
I set out to get you with a fine tooth comb
I was soft inside, there was somethin' going on

290. So what am I so afraid of?
I'm afraid that I'm not sure of
A love there is no cure for

291. In a restaurant in a West End town
Call the police, there's a madman around
Running down underground to a dive bar
In a West End town

292. All my bags are packed, I'm ready to go
     I'm standing here outside your door
     I hate to wake you up to say goodbye

293. Instead of makin' me better, you keep makin' me ill
     You keep makin' me ill

294. Something's gotten into my life
     Cutting its way through my dreams like a knife
     Turning me up, turning me down
     Making me smile and making me frown

295. I'll take you down, I'll take you down
     Where no one's ever gone before
     And if you want more, if you want more
     More, more, more

296. Since you've gone I've been lost without a trace
     I dream at night, I can only see your face
     I look around, but it's you I can't replace
     I feel so cold, and I long for your embrace

297. I was dreamin' when I wrote this
     Forgive me if it goes astray
     But when I woke up this mornin'
     Coulda sworn it was judgment day

298. I never meant 2 cause u any sorrow
     I never meant 2 cause u any pain
     I only wanted 2 one time see u laughing
     I only wanted 2 see u laughing

299. Trailers for sale or rent rooms to left fifty cents
     No phones no pool no pets I ain't got no cigarettes

300. And so it was that later
     As the Miller told his tale
     That her face, at first just ghostly
     Turned a ......

301. Are you ready hey are you ready for this?
     Are you hanging on the edge of your seat?
     Out of the doorway the bullets rip
     To the sound of the beat yeah

302. There goes my baby
     She knows how to Rock'n'Roll
     She drives my crazy
     She gives me hot and cold fever
     Then she leaves me in a cool cool sweat

303. I've paid my dues
     Time after time
     I've done my sentence
     But committed no crime

304. When the day is long
     And the night, the night is yours alone
     When you're sure you've had enough of this life
     Well hang on

305. The distance in your eyes
     Oh no I've said too much, I said it all
     That's me in the corner
     That's me in the spotlight

306. You should have seen by the look in my eyes baby
     There was something missing.
     You should have known by the talk of my
      voice maybe
     But you didn't listen.

307. The damn thing gone wild
Bama lamb
Said weren't none of mine
Bama lamb
The damn thing gone blind
Bama lamb

308. When you kiss me I just gotta
Kiss me I just gotta
Kiss me I just gotta say:

309. Standing in line to
See the show tonight
And there's a light on
Heavy glow

310. Sittin' in the mornin' sun
I'll be sittin' when the evenin' come
Watching the ships roll in
And then I watch 'em roll away again

311. You live your life in the songs you hear
On the rock and roll radio.
And when a young girl doesn't have any friends
That's a really nice place to go.

312. Holly came from Miami F.L.A.
Hitch-hiked her way across the U.S.A.
Plucked her eyebrows on the way

313. Oh it doesn't matter what you wear, just as long as
you are there.
So come on every guy, grab a girl,
Everywhere, around the world

44

314. I woke up this morning and realized what I had done
I stood alone in the cold gray dawn
I knew I'd lost my morning sun

315. Take a look at her hair, it's real,
And if you don't believe what I say, just feel.
I'm gonna lock her up in a trunk, so no big hunk,
Can steal her away from me.

316. Don't look back or turn away
Life can be yours if you'll only stay
He is calling you, calling you

317. Everybody sing, everybody dance
Lose yourself in wild romance
We're goin' to party, karamu, fiesta, forever
Come on and sing along!

318. I can see it in your eyes
I can see it in your smile
You're all I've ever wanted
And my arms are open wide

319. Oh, my love, my darling
I've hungered for your touch
A long, lonely time
And time goes by so slowly
And time can do so much

320. I'm a model you know what I mean
And I do my little turn on the catwalk
Yeah on the catwalk on the catwalk yeah
I do my little turn on the catwalk

321. You never close your eyes anymore when I kiss your lips
And there's no tenderness like before in your fingertips

322. I know it's late, I know you're weary
I know your plans don't include me
Still here we are, both of us lonely
Longing for shelter from all that we see

323. And I was there and not dancing with anyone
You took a little, then you took me over
You set your mark on stealing my heart away
Crying, trying, anything for you

324. I take you on a skyride
A feeling like you're spellbound
The sunshine is a lady
Who ROX you like a baby

325. Walking like a man,
Hitting like a hammer,
She's a juvenile scam.
Never was a quitter,

326. She starts swingin
With the boys in tune
And her feet just fly up in the air
Singin hey diddle diddle with a kitty in the middle
And they swingin like it just don't care

327. Your voice is warm and tender
A love I could not forsake
Cuz I'm your lady and you are my man
Whenever you reach for me I'll do all that I can

328. Your kisses ring, round and round and round my head.
Touching the very part of me.
It's making my soul sing.
Tearing the very heart of me.
I'm crying out for more

329. You live in a fancy apartment
Off the Boulevard of St. Michel
Where you keep your Rolling Stones records
And a friend of Sacha Distel

330. If a picture paints a thousand words
Then why can't I paint you?
The words will never show
The you I've come to know.

331. Miles and miles of empty space in between us
The telephone can't take the place of your smile
But you know I won't be travelin' forever
It's cold out, but hold out, and do like I do

332. He said one more job ought to get it
One last shot 'fore we quit it
One more for the road

333. There used to be a greying tower alone on the sea.
You became the light on the dark side of me.
Love remained a drug that's the high and not the pill.

334. Strolling along country roads with my baby
It starts to rain, it begins to pour
Without an umbrella we're soaked to the skin
I feel a shiver run up my spine
I feel the warmth of her hand in mine

335. I know it's late, I know you're weary
     I know your plans don't include me
     Still here we are, both of us lonely
     Longing for shelter from all that we see

336. At break of day when that man drove away,
       I was waiting
     I cross the street to her house and she opened the door
     She stood there laughing
     I felt the knife in my hand and she laughed no more

337. Honey came in and she caught me red-handed
     Sleeping with the girl next door
     Picture this we were both butt-naked
     Bangin on the bathroom door

338. I'm a-walkin' in the rain,
     Tears are fallin' and I feel the pain,
     Wishin' you were here by me,
     To end this misery
     And I wonder

339. I met him at the candy store
     He turned around and smiled at me
     You get the picture? (yes, we see)

340. The higher you build your barriers
     The taller I become
     The farther you take my rights away
     The faster I will run

341. But you gave away the things you loved and
       one of them was me
     I had some dreams, they were clouds in my coffee
     Clouds in my coffee

342. Y   ou just slip out the back, Jack
     Make a new plan, Stan
     You don't need to be coy, Roy
     Just get yourself free

343. And I'm laying out my winter clothes, wishing
     I was gone, goin' home
     Where the New York city winters aren't
     bleedin' me, leadin' me to go home

344. We'd like to know
     A little bit about you
     For our files.
     We'd like to help you learn
     To help yourself.

345. Will you stand above me?
     Look my way, never love me
     Rain keeps falling, rain keeps falling
     Down, down, down

346. When I come home
     A little late at night
     Cos we only act like children
     When we argue fuss and fight

347. I've got you deep in the heart of me
     So deep in my heart, that you're really a part of me

348. And if we go someplace to dance, I know that
     there's a chance
     You won't be leaving with me
     And afterwards we drop into a quiet little place
     And have a drink or two

349. I'm laughing at clouds
     So dark up above
     The sun's in my heart
     And I'm ready for love

350. He'll trade the world
     For the good thing he's found
     If she's bad he can't see it
     She can do no wrong
     Turn his back on his best friend
     If he put her down

351. Any damsel that's in distress
     Be out of that dress when she meet Jim West
     Rough neck so go check the law and abide
     Watch your step with flex and get a hole in your side

352. Don't let them say your hair's too long
     'Cause I don't care, with you I can't go wrong
     Then put your little hand in mine
     There ain't no hill or mountain we can't climb

353. I really lost my head last night
     You've got a right to start believin'
     There's still a little love left, even so

354. Mary was the girl who taught me
     All I had to know
     She put me right on my first mistake

355. Heartbeat, increasing heartbeat
     You hear the thunder of stampeding rhinos,
     Elephants and tacky tigers

356. My loneliness is killin me (and I)
     I must confess I still believe (still believe)
     When I'm not with you I lose my mind

357. If you want my future forget my past
     If you wanna get with me better make it fast
     Now don't go wasting my precious time
     Get your act together, we could be just fine

358. And she's watching him with those eyes
     And she's lovin' him with that body, I just know it
     Yeah 'n' he's holding her in his arms late, late at night

359. At night we ride through mansions of glory in
        suicide machines
     Sprung from cages out on highway 9,
     Chrome wheeled, fuel injected
     And steppin' out over the line

360. I check my look in the mirror
     I wanna change my clothes, my hair, my face
     Man I ain't getting nowhere
     I'm just living in a dump like this

361. Got in a little hometown jam
     So they put a rifle in my hand
     Sent me off to a foreign land
     To go and kill the yellow man

362. Been around the world and I, I, I
     I can't find my baby
     I don't know when, I don't know why
     Why he's gone away

363. You're my baby, you're my pet
     We fell in love on the night we met
     You touched my hand, my heart went pop
     Ooh, when we kissed I could not stop

364. Knee deep in the hoopla, sinking in your fight
     Too many runaways eating up the night
     Marconi plays the mamba, listen to the radio,
       don't you remember

365. Here we are in a room full of strangers,
     I'm standing in the dark where your eyes couldn't see me
     Well, I have to follow you
     Though you did not want me to,
     But that won't stop my lovin' you
     I just can't stay away

366. You've been tellin' me you're a genius since you
       were seventeen
     In all the time I've known you, I still don't know
       what you mean
     The weekend at the college didn't turn out like
       you planned
     The things that pass for knowledge, I can't understand

367. And if I ever lose my hands
     Lose my power
     Lose my land
     Oh if I ever lose my hands
     Ooh I won't have to work no more.

368. Hello, everyone,
     This is your action news reporter with all the news
     That is news across the nation,
     On the scene at the supermarket.

369. 'Cause your love is better
     Than any love I know.
     It's like thunder and lightning,
     The way you love me is frightening.

370. Kick off your shoes and sit right down
     Loosen off that pretty French gown
     Let me pour you a good long drink
     Ooh baby don't you hesitate cause

371. I still want you by my side
     Just to help me dry the tears that I've cried
     And I'm sure going to give you a try
     And if you want I'll try to love again

372. The big bosomed lady with the Dutch accent
     Who tried to change my point of view
     Her ad lib lines were well rehearsed
     But my heart cried out for you

373. Lays me down
     With my mind she runs
     Throughout the night
     No need to fight
     Never a frown

374. Who can I turn to and where can I stay?
     I heard a place is open all night and all day
     There's a place you can go where the cops don't know
     You can act real wild they don't treat you like a child

375. Life is a moment in space
     When the dream is gone
     It's a lonelier place

376. Some say love, it is a river, that drowns the tender reed
Some say love, it is a razor, that leads your soul to bleed

377. But I'll be lonely without you
And I'll need your love to see me through
So please believe me
My heart is in your hands
I'll be missing you

378. Sittin' here, eatin' my heart out waitin'
Waitin' for some lover to call
Dialed about a thousand numbers lately
Almost rang the phone off the wall

379. When I was young, it seemed that life was so wonderful,
A miracle, oh it was beautiful, magical.
And all the birds in the trees, well they'd be singing so happily,
Joyfully, playfully watching me

380. When I go to sleep at night you're always a part of
my dream
Holding me tight and telling me everything I
wanna hear
Don't forget me baby, all you gotta do is call
You know how I feel about you, if I can do anything at all

381. Well you're slim and you're weak
You got the teeth
Of the Hydra upon you
You're dirty sweet
And you're my girl

382. Well we know where we're goin'
     But we don't know where we've been
     And we know what we're knowin'
     But we can't say what we've seen

383. Close your eyes and think of me
     And soon I will be there
     To brighten up even your darkest nights

384. These are the things I can do without
     Come on
     I'm talking to you
     Come on

385. I've got sunshine on a cloudy day
     When it's cold outside
     I've got the month of May
     I guess you'll say
     What can make me feel this way

386. But there's one thing I know
     The blues they send to meet me won't defeat me
     It won't be long till happiness steps up to greet me

387. When will our hearts beat together?
     Are we in love or just friends?
     Is this my beginning
     Or is this the end?

388. Running just as fast as we can
     Holdin' on to one another's hand
     Tryin' to get away into the night
     And then you put your arms around me
     And we tumble to the ground
     And then you say

389. I hear the drums echoing tonight
But she hears only whispers of some quiet conversation
She's coming in twelve - thirty flight

390. Well it's all right, riding around in the breeze
Well it's all right, if you live the life you please
Well it's all right, doing the best you can
Well it's all right, as long as you lend a hand

391. He got friendly, holdin' my hand,
Well she got friendly, down in the sand
He was sweet, just turned eighteen
Well she was good, you know what I mean

392. I think I love you
But I wanna know for sure
Come on, hold me tight
I love you

393. What you will and what you won't
What you do and what you don't
What you can and what you can't
This is what you need to know:
Loved you though it didn't show

394. Twenty-five for speed limit
Motorcycle not allowed in it
You go to store on Friday
You go to church on Sunday

395. You don't look at their faces
And you don't ask their names
You don't think of them as human
You don't think of them at all

56

396. I call you, when I need you my hearts on fire
     You come to me, come to me, wild and wild
     You come to me, give me everything I need
     Give me a lifetime of promises and a world of dreams

397. You think you're a genius-you drive me up the wall
     You're a regular original, a know-it-all
     Oh-oo-oh, you think you're special
     Oh-oo-oh, you think you're something else

398. My one and only prayer
     Is that some day you'll care
     My hope's my dream's come true
     My one and only you

399. Turnaround,
     Every now and then I get a little bit lonely and
       you're never coming round
     Turnaround,
     Every now and then I get a little bit tired of listening
       to the sound of my tears

400. They say our love won`t pay the rent
     Before it's earn`d our money`s always spent
     I guess that's so, we don't have a lot
     But at least I'm sure of all the things we got

401. The feeling has gone only you and I.
     It means nothing to me.
     This means nothing to me.

402. There comes a time when we need a certain call
     When the world must come together as one
     There are people dying
     Oh, and it's time to lend a hand to life

403. There's a world outside your window
And it's a world of dread and fear
Where the only water flowing is the bitter sting of tears

404. I get up, and nothing gets me down
You got it tough, I've seen the toughest around
And I know, baby, just how you feel
You've got to roll with the punches to get to what's real

405. Let's enjoy it while we can
Won't you help me sing my song
From the dark end of the street

406. I've got your picture, I've got your picture
I'd like a million of you all round my cell
I want a doctor to take your picture
So I can look at you from inside as well

407. Marlene watches from the wall
Her mocking smile says it all
As the records the rise and fall
Of every soldier passing

408. They want you, they want you
They want you as a new recruit

409. You can get yourself cleaned, you can have a
good meal,
You can do whatever you feel ...

410. Who knows what tomorrow brings
In a world, few hearts survive
All I know is the way I feel
When it's real, I keep it alive

58

411. When I was bein' what you want me to be ?
     Suddenly everything I ever wanted has passed me by,
     This world may end, not you and I.

412. Humidity is rising – Barometer's getting low
     According to all sources, the street's the place to go
     Cause tonight for the first time
     Just about half-past ten

413. Didn't I come resisting this sight of wonder
     Didn't I come insisting the higher decision
     Didn't I come resisting this sight of wonder
     To your life

414. You put the boom boom into my heart
     You send my soul sky high when your loving starts
     Jitterbug into my brain
     Goes a bang bang bang till my feet do the same

415. This year
     To save me from tears
     I'll give it to someone special

416. I like the way you move
     Pretty baby
     It's party time and not one minute we can lose
     Be my baby

417. And the answer to all my dreams
     You're my sun, my moon, my guiding star
     My kind of wonderful, that's what you are.

418. Goin' down the only road I've ever known,
Like a Drifter I was born to walk alone
An' I've made up my mind
I ain't wasting no more time

419. He stands like a statue,
Becomes part of the machine.
Feeling all the bumpers
Always playing clean.

420. Yeah, they were dancin' and singin' and movin'
to the groovin'
And just when it hit me somebody turned around
and shouted

421. Set me free, why don't you babe?
Get out my life, why don't you babe?
'Cause you don't really love me

422. You feel like heaven to touch
I wanna hold you so much
At last love has arrived
And I thank God I'm alive
You're just too good to be true

423. When the sun beats down
And burns the tar up on the roof
And your shoes get so hot
You wish your tired feet were fireproof

424. Well, lookabell, lookabell, lookabell, lookabell
Oooooh Weeeeee
Lookabell, lookabell, lookabell oooooooweeee

425. And I'll be your friend
     I'll help you carry on
     For it won't be long
     'Til I'm gonna need
     Somebody to

426. Thirteen month old baby, broke the lookin' glass
     Seven years of bad luck, the good things in your past.

427. But if you love him, you'll forgive him
     Even though he's hard to understand
     And if you love him, oh be proud of him
     Cause after all he's just a man

428. I've been to Hollywood, I've been to Redwood
     I crossed the ocean for a heart of gold
     I've been in my mind, it's such a fine line

429. Hey!, if we can solve any problem
     Then why do we lose so many tears
     Oh, and so you go again
     When the leading man appears

430. Everybody all around the world, stand up
      all my brothers
     Joining our hands, united we're stronger
     Fighting for peace, caring about our loved ones
     Trusting ourselves, sharing our feeling, believe me

431. You got to whip it up and hit me like a ton of lead,
     If I blow my top will you let it go to your head?

432. Clean shirt, new shoes
And I don't know where I am goin' to.
Silk suit, black tie,
I don't need a reason why.
They come runnin' just as fast as they can
Coz every girl crazy 'bout a...

Quiz 2

Lines Back-to-Back

433. Her hair is Harlow gold,
     Her lips a sweet surprise

434. Nothing really matters,
     Nothing really matters to me

435. They were prayin' for the lovers, in the
     Valley of the gun

436. Under the moonlight,
     The serious moonlight

437. The five years we've been together
     Have been such good times

438. No one to kill or die for
     And no religion too

439. I suppose I could collect my books
     And get back on back to school

440. Can't salute you,
     Can't find a flag,

441. When you're weary, feeling small
     When tears are in your eyes, I will dry them all

442. People dancing all in the street,
     See the rhythm all in their feet

443. There's a killer on the road
     His brain is squirming like a toad

444. Can you hear
     Can you hear the thunder

445. I got sunshine
     On a cloudy day

446. There she stood in the street
     Smiling from her head to her feet

447. You got a heart of glass or a heart of stone
     Just wait till I get you home

448. Hair of gold,
     Lips like cherries

449. In the twist of separation
     You excelled at being free

450. And frolicked in the autumn mist
     In a land called Honah Lee

451. Once I had a love and it was divine
     Soon found out I was losing my mind

452. When I'm watching my TV
and the man comes on to tell me

453. Hope you need my love babe
Just like I need you

454. I guess that's so, we don't have a pot
But at least I'm sure of all the things we got

455. Gazing from my window to the streets below
On a freshly fallen silent shroud of snow

456. 'cause if there's one thing that she don't need
It's another hungry mouth to feed

457. If you were drowning
I wouldn't lend a hand

458. Under a blood red sky
A crowd has gathered in black and white

459. Letting the days go by water flowing underground
Into the blue again after the money's gone

460. Gonna use it up, wear it out
Ain't nothing left in this whole world I care about

461. I woke up in a Soho doorway
A policeman knew my name

462. He says he's a beautician and sells you nutrition
     And keeps all your dead hair for making up underwear

463. They paved paradise
     And put up a parking lot

464. She can kill with a smile
     She can wound with her eyes

465. I know it sounds absurd
     But please tell me who I am

466. Trying to see it my way
     Do I have to keep on talking till I can't go on

467. Life is a mystery
     Everyone must stand alone

468. Then she lit up a candle
     And showed me the way

469. My! How can I ever refuse
     I feel like I win, win or lose

470. Don't wanna see no blood,
     Don't be a macho man

471. He said
     'girl you better look to have fun no matter what you do

472. Take your shoes off, do not fear
     Bring that bottle over here

473. I awoke last night to the sound of thunder
     How far off I sat and wondered

474. Ground control to Major Tom
     Take your protein pills and put your helmet on

475. And my family listened fifty times to my two
     song repertoire
     And I told my Mum her only son was gonna be a star

476. I walked out this morning
     And I wrote down this song

477. Like a storm in the desert
     Like a sleepy blue ocean

478. Why do birds suddenly appear
     Everytime you are near

479. I am a linesman for the county
     And I drive the main road

480. Cos when I get you alone
     You know I'll be ok

481. Let your love fly like a bird on the wing
     And let your love bind you to all living things

482. The finest years I ever knew
Were all the years I had with you

483. And I dream of the things I'll do
With a subway token and a dollar tucked inside
my shoe

484. Those were such happy times
And not so long ago

485. A love like ours is love that's hard to find
How could we let it slip away

486. I once was lost, but now am found,
Was blind, but now can see.

487. All the downtown ladies call him "Treetop Lover"
All the men just call him "Sir"

488. Oh, I love my Rosie child
She got the way to make me happy

489. The marchin' band came down along Main Street
The soldier-blues fell in behind

490. I learned how to laugh
And I learned how to cry

491. And so I came to see him to listen for a while.
And there he was this young boy, a stranger to my eyes

492. Tell me no secrets, tell me some lies
     Give me no reasons, give me alibis.

493. I ain't the worst that you've seen.
     Oh can't you see what I mean?

494. She's got me with nothing left to win
     And nothing else to lose

495. I check my look in the mirror
     I wanna change my clothes, my hair, my face

496. Rain keeps falling
     Rain keeps falling

497. I have spoke with the tongue of angels
     I have held the hand of a devil

498. You should have seen by the look in my eyes, baby
     There was somethin' missin'

499. Got on board a westbound seven forty seven
     Didn't think before deciding what to do

500. The road is long
     With many a winding turn

501. It'll take you a couple of vodka and tonics
     To set you on your feet again

502. Sometimes I think it's a shame
When I get feelin' better when I'm feelin' no pain

503. His name was Rico, he wore a diamond
He was escorted to his chair, he saw Lola dancin' there

504. And A Bell Was Ringing In The Village Square
For The Rabbits On The Run

505. You gave them all those old time stars
Through wars of worlds - invaded by Mars

506. How my poor heart breaks
With every step you take

507. Your lights are on, but you're not home
Your mind is not your own

508. Every time you call my name
I heat up like a burnin' flame

509. And it don't take money, don't take fame
Don't need no credit card to ride this train

510. I better read between the lines
In case I need it when I'm older

511. And while Lenin read a book on Marx
The quartet practiced in the park

512. Are you sure
     Yes I'm sure down deep inside

513. If you received my letter
     Telling you I'd soon be free

514. But he started shaking
     His big heart was breaking

515. But you gave away the things you loved
     And one of them was me

516. Can it be that it was all so simple then
     Or has time rewritten every line

517. I shoulda learned to play the guitar
     I shoulda learned to play them drums

518. It doesn't matter what you wear,
     Just as long as you are there

519. She says: We've got to hold on to what we've got
     'Cause it doesn't make a difference if we make it or not

520. I got my first real six-string
     Bought it at the five-and-dime

521. All the things that we've been through
     You should understand me like I understand you

522. My little baby sister can do it with ease
It's easier than learning your a b c's

523. The blues they send to meet me won't defeat me
It won't be long till happiness steps up to greet me

524. Listen to the ground
There is movement all around

525. And now that we've come to the end of our rainbow
There's something I must say out loud

526. I should have changed that stupid lock
I should have made you leave your key

527. How did ya' know I needed you so badly
How did ya' know I gave my heart gladly

528. He said he's goin' back to find
Ooh, what's left of his world, the world he left behind

529. I call you, when I need you
My heart's on fire

530. A full commitment's what I'm thinking of
You wouldn't get this from any other guy

531. Poor old Johnny Ray
Sounded sad upon the radio

532. It's time to come together
     It's up to you, what's your pleasure

533. Then you say 'go slow'
     I fall behind, the second hand unwinds

534. People are the same where ever we go
     There is good and bad in ev'ryone

535. We've been sailing with a cargo full of,
     Love and devotion

536. I think I can make it now, the pain is gone
     All of the bad feelings have disappeared

537. Between the parted pages and were pressed,
     In love's hot fevered iron, like a striped pair of pants

538. You can get yourself clean
     You can have a good meal

539. You're my sun, my moon, my guiding star
     My kind of wonderful, that's what you are

540. After three days in the desert fun
     I was looking at a river bed

541. But his blood runs thru' my instrument
     And his song is in my soul

542. The one you warned me all about
The one you said I could do without

543. Well it takes a strong man baby
But I'm showing you the door

544. Some say love, it is a hunger,
An endless aching need

545. Little things I should have said and done
I just never took the time

546. I can see it in your eyes
I can see it in your smile

547. She took me to her doctor
And he told me of a cure

548. I lost myself in a familiar song
I closed my eyes and I slipped away

549. Now the promoter don't mind
And the union don't mind

550. My son turned ten just the other day
He said, "Thanks for the ball, Dad, come on let's play

551. She puts on her make-up
And brushes her long blonde hair

552. He can play honky tonk just like anything
     Saving it up for Friday night

553. If you want to know if he loves you so
     It's in his kiss

554. The whispers in the morning
     Of lovers sleeping tight

555. Bittersweet memories, that is all I'm taking with me.
     So, goodbye. Please, don't cry

556. In the middle of the night
     I go walking in my sleep

557. This torch we'll always carry
     For our nation's golden child

558. Although she's dressed up to the nines
     At sixes and sevens with you

559. Problem is, I've been fooled before
     By fair weathered friends and faint hearted lovers

560. If your life was bad to you
     Just think what tomorrow will do

561. If I leave here tomorrow
     Would you still remember me

562. I tried to show you just how much I care
     I'm tired of words and I'm too hoarse to shout

563. Some people call me Maurice
     'Cause I speak of the pompitous of love

564. Gazing at people some hand in hand
     Just what I'm going through they can't understand

565. I can't light no more of your darkness
     All my pictures seem to fade to black and white

566. Touch me now,
     I close my eyes

567. Looks like we made it
     Look how far we've come my baby

568. Fish are jumping and the cotton is high
     Your daddy's rich and your mama's good-looking

569. How the thought of you does things to me
     Never before has someone been more.....

570. Every now and then I get a little bit lonely
     And you're never comin' 'round

571. Would you dance if asked you to dance
     Would you run and never look back

572. A mole, digging in a hole
     Digging up my soul now, going down, excavation

573. And I've been wrong, I've been down
     Into the bottom of every bottle

574. We're meant to be together, I'll be there and
     you'll be near
     And that's the deal my dear, thereover, hereunder

575. Houston can you hear me
     Ground-control can you feel me, need permission
     to land

576. Cause I remember when we used to sit
     In a government yard in Trenchtown

577. You touch my hand and I'm a king
     Your kiss to me is worth a fortune

578. Gold Coast slave ship bound for cotton fields
     Sold in the market down in New Orleans

579. Sprung from cages out on highway 9,
     Chrome wheeled, fuel injected and steppin' out over
     the line

580. I was kissin' Valentino
     By a crystal blue Italian stream

581. All alone I have cried
     Silent tears full of pride

582. I didn't really mean to hurt you
   I didn't wanna see you go

583. There are mountains in the way
   But we climb a step every day

584. And I've got such a long way to go
   To make it to the border of Mexico

585. When you go you're gone forever.
   You string along, you string along

586. Que tu cuerpo es pa' darle
   alegria y cosa Buena

587. A superdope homeboy from the Oaktown
   And I'm known as such and this is a beat-uh

588. I'd been married long time ago
   Where did you come from, where did you go

589. My loneliness is killing me (and I)
   I must confess, I still believe

590. Now don't go wasting my precious time
   Get your act together, we could be just fine

591. Sometimes the snow comes down in June
   Sometimes the sun goes round the moon

592. Don't tell me it's not worth tryin' for
     You can't tell me it's not worth dyin' for

593. I'm a colt in your stable
     I'm what Cain was to Abel

594. I tried to give you consolation
     When your old man had let you down.

595. But I'm sure he's Bill or Billy or Mac or buddy
     And he's plain ugly to me

596. I told them you were living downtown
     Driving all the old men crazy

597. And so I wake in the morning and I step outside
     And I take a deep breath and I get real high

598. Like a cheap distraction for a new affair
     She knew it would finish before it began

599. But I wont do that,
     I wont do that

600. And all the roads we have to walk are winding
     And all the lights that lead us there are blinding

601. If I get drunk yes I know I'm gonna be
     I'm gonna be the man who gets drunk next to you

602. When the day is long and the night,
The night is yours alone,

603. You'll remember me when the west wind moves
Upon the fields of barley

604. When you hit the ground
It's alright...it's alright...it's alright

605. That's me in the corner
That's me in the spotlight

606. But I made me a vow to the moon and stars
I'd search the honky tonks and bars

607. Gonna get rowdy, Gonna get a little unruly
Get it fired up in a hurry, Wanna get.....

608. You're watching your back, like you can't relax
You're trying to be cool, you look like a fool to me

609. Girl I refuse, you must have me confused
With some other guy

610. We're talking away
I don't know what I'm to say, I'll say it anyway

611. Some dance to remember
Some dance to forget

612. I, I love the colourful clothes she wears
And the way the sunlight plays upon her hair

613. I'm gonna take a little time,
A little time to look around me

614. Where you gonna run to now, where you gonna go
I'm goin' way down south, way down to Mexico way

615. Won't you then stay forever
And ever and ever and ever

616. When the world seems to shine
Like you've had too much wine

617. Through early morning fog I see
Visions of the things to be

618. Some boys try and some boys lie
But I don't let them play

619. There goes my baby, there goes my heart
They've gone forever, so far apart

620. Viene diego rumbeando
With the magic in his eyes

621. Used to have a little now I have a lot
No matter where I go I know where I came from

622. Now that spring is in the air
     Pretty girls are everywhere

623. These days, she says, I feel my life
     Just like a river running through

624. But when I woke up this mornin',
     Could've sworn it was Judgment Day

625. Got the wings of heaven on my shoes.
     I'm a dancin' man and I just can't lose.

626. For well you know that it's a fool who plays it cool
     By making his world a little colder

627. I was wrong and I find
     Just one thing makes me forget

628. Come blow the horn, start celebrating
     Right this way, your table's waiting

629. Do you feel my heart beating?
     Do you understand?

630. Fish are jumpin'
     And the cotton is high

631. No stop signs, speed limit, nobody's gonna
       slow us down
     Like a wheel, gonna spin it, nobody's gonna
       mess me round

632. I'm the dandy highwayman who you're too scared
    to mention
    I spend my cash on looking flash and grabbing
    your attention

633. Now the only thing a gambler needs
    Is a suitcase and a trunk

634. We're after that same rainbow's end,
    Waiting round the bend, my Huckleberry Finn....

635. You see I feel sad when you're sad
    I feel glad when you're glad

636. Santa Cruz and Trestles, Australia's Narabine
    All over Manhattan and down Doheny Way

637. Go down to the river, babe,
    Honey, I will meet you there.

638. Baby I was afraid before
    But I'm not afraid anymore

639. I'm going out tonight-I'm feelin' alright
    Gonna let it all hang out

640. Don't stop never give up
    Hold you head high and reach the top

641. Coast to coast, LA to Chicago, western male.
    Across the north and south, to Key Largo

642. I bought a ticket to the world
    But now I've come back again

643. We could stay inside and play games, I don't know
    And you could have a change of heart

644. Just say the words, and we'll beat the birds
    Down to Acapulco Bay

645. Listen to the wind blow, watch the sun rise
    Run in the shadows, damn your love, damn your lies

646. We are young, heartache to heartache we stand
    No promises, no demands

647. Worry, why do I let myself worry
    Wond'rin', what in the world did I do

648. The moon is right, the spirits up
    We're here tonight and that's enough

649. You could have a big dipper
    Going up and down, all around the bends

650. The shadows follow me,
    And the night won't set me free!

651. Call the police, there's a madman around
    Running down underground to a dive bar, in a
    West End town

652. I didn't mean to hurt you
     I'm sorry that I made you cry

653. I never meant 2 cause u any sorrow
     I never meant 2 cause u any pain

654. Stay away from my window
     Stay away from my back door too

655. Life's too short for you to die
     So grab yourself an alibi

656. Catch the breeze and the winter chills
     In colors on the snowy linen land

657. We gotta move these refrigerators
     We gotta move these colour TV's

658. She'll only come out at night
     The lean and hungry type

659. Jump in the shower and the blood starts pumpin'
     Out on the streets the traffic starts jumpin'

660. Frank Zappa and the Mothers were at the best
     place around
     But some stupid with a flare gun burned the place
     to the ground

661. When I was young I never needed anyone
     And makin' love was just for fun, those days are gone

662. My temperature's risin,
     The juke box's blowin a fuse

663. From Soho down to Brighton
     I must have played them all.

664. I kinda get to thinking
     Of all the things you said

665. Well we drank champagne and danced all night
     Under electric candlelight

666. And you may find yourself in a beautiful house,
     With a beautiful wife

667. I cross the street to her house and
     she opened the door

668. You've got a smile so bright,
     You know you could have been a candle

669. I hear the drums echoing tonight
     But she hears only whispers of some quiet conversation

670. The somewhere near Salinas, Lord, I let her slip away,
     She was lookin' for the love I hope she'll find,

671. Down below the cars in the city go rushing by
     I sit here alone and I wonder why

672. Ooh, it gets dark! It gets lonely,
On the other side from you.

673. All I know is the way I feel
When it's real I keep it alive

674. The beat was goin' strong, playin' my favorite song
An' I could tell it wouldn't be long

675. Here in my car I feel safest of all
I can lock all my doors, it's the only way to live

676. Hope you got your things together.
Hope you are quite prepared to die.

677. I don't care what people say,
To me you're more than a child

678. The torn dress, the shattered look
Was more than he could stand

679. There's a fog along the horizon,
A strange glow in the sky

680. Ain't it good ain't it right
That you are with me here tonight

681. My whole life has crashed
Won't you pick the pieces up 'cause it feels just like I'm

682. Winter's cityside, crystal bits of snowflakes
     All around my head and in the wind

683. I go weak, I go weak
     I go weak, I go weak

684. There goes my baby, there goes my heart
     They're gone forever, so far apart

685. Got on a board a west bound seven forty seven
     Didn't think before deciding what to do

686. The clumsy boots, peek-a-boo roots that people think
     so dashing
     So what's the point of robbery when nothing is
     worth taking?

687. And I was you and I was you –
     If they were me and I was you

688. Once in every lifetime
     Comes a love like this.

689. Yes Sir, Already told you in the first verse
     And in the chorus but I will give you one more chance.

690. Take these tears from my eyes and let me see
     Just a spark of the love that used to be

691. And when the sun comes shining through
     We'll know what to do

692. Get back scruffy, back scruffy,
     Get back u flea infested mungrel

693. Virgil Caine is my name and I served on the
     Danville train,
     Till so much cavalry came and they tore up the
     tracks again

694. Mem'ries light the corners of my mind.
     Misty water color mem'ries

695. 'Til the day I die you're my reality
     Yet I'm in a dream

696. Good loving, I got a truck load
     And when you get it, you got something

697. They took the credit for your second symphony.
     Rewritten by machine and new technology

698. Put your glad rags on and join me hon',
     We'll have some fun when the clock strikes one

699. Something in the wind has learned my name
     And it's tellin' me that things are not the same

700. Who's gonna tell you things
     Aren't so great

701. And if I ever lose my eyes
     If my colours all run dry

Quiz 3

Great Artists, Great Hits

One line intros

721. Looking from a window above, it's like a story of love

722. Desert loving in your eyes all the way

723. You need coolin' baby, I'm not foolin'

724. It's late in the evening, she's wondering what clothes to wear.

725. I come home in the morning light

726. When I wake up in the morning, love

727. Oh, don't it hurt deep inside, to see someone do something to hurt

728. The Child is a King, the Carollers sing

729. In the day we sweat it out in the streets of a runaway American dream

730. Gold coast slave ship bound for cotton fields,

Elvis Presley

741. A little less fight and a little more spark

742. You know I can be found, sitting home all alone

743. Who do you thank when you have such luck?

744. Little things I should have said and done

745. When they said you was high classed

746. Look away, look away, look away Dixieland

747. Spider Murphy played the tenor saxophone

748. Is your heart filled with pain, shall I come back again?

749. I'll be yours through all the years, till the end of time

750. Drink my liquor, From an old fruitjar.

751. In downtown Birmingham

752. It's burning through to my soul

753. I'm leaving town, baby, I'm leaving town for sure

754. Tell me, tell me that your sweet love hasn't died

755. Baby it's just you I'm thinking of.

The Beatles

756. Do you need anybody,
     I just need somebody to love

757. There's nothing you can do that can't be done.

758. You don't know how lucky you are boys

759. I am he as you are he as you are me
     and we are all together

760. Friday night arrives without a suitcase

761. Nothing is real and nothing to get hungabout

762. Why she had to go I don't know she wouldn't say
763. Get on home Loretta

764. Say you don't want no diamond ring, and I'll be
     satisfied,

765. Waits at the window, wearing a face she keeps in
     a jar by the door

The Eagles

784. Beautiful faces and
loud, empty places

785. She got a lot of pretty, pretty boys,
that she calls friends

786. Late at night a big old house gets lonely
I guess ev'ry form of refuge has its price

787. You got your demons, You got desires
Well, I got a few of my own

788. And I found out a long time ago
What a woman can do to your soul

789. You can spend all your time making money
You can spend all your love making time

790. Ev'ry night when the sun goes down
Just another lonely boy in town

U2

791. New York, like a Christmas tree
     Tonight this city belongs to me

792. See the world in green and blue
     See China, right in front of you

793. At the corner of your lips
     As the orbit of your hips

794. If you walkaway, walkaway
     I walkaway, walkaway

795. A world in white gets underway I want to be with you,
     Be with you night and day

796. One man come, he to justify
     One man to overthrow

797. I wanted to run but she made me crawl

798. I see the dust cloud disappear
     Without a trace

799. But all the promises we make
     From the cradle to the grave

800. If I could through myself
     Set your spirit free

Quiz 4

Gimme a Line

811. That's me in the corner, that's me in the spotlight

812. Because maybe, you're gonna be the one
who saves me

813. Since you've gone I been lost without a trace

814. U don't have 2 be rich 2 be my girl

815. Kick off your shoes, and sit right down

816. Steve walks warily down the street

817. And the wicked wind whispers and moans

818. All alone I have cried, silent tears full of pride

819. How about a pair of pink sidewinders

820. Didn't know how lost I was, until I found you

821. When I come to call she won't forsake me but when
you take the blues and make a song

848. Now I believe in miracles and a miracle,
has happened tonight

849. You're the only thing in this whole world that's
pure and good and right

850. Oh God I think I'm falling out of the sky, I close my eyes

851. Come writers and critics who prophesize with your pen

852. So why don't you use it, try not to bruise it

853. Call my name or walk on by

854. Honey came in and she caught me red-handed,
sleeping with the girl next door

855. Then you flew your lear jet up to Nova Scotia

856. Well it seems a long time ago you were the lonely one

857. It was a theme she had, on a scheme he had,
told in a foreign land

858. Find us a dream that don't asks no questions, yeah

859. It'll take you a couple of vodka and tonics to set
you on your feet again

860. Now hold on a minute before we go much further,
     give me a dime so I can phone my mother

861. In between, what I find is pleasing and I'm feeling fine

862. In my imagination there is no complication

863. Man, I'm just tired and bored with myself

864. Well that's the way that I want it to stay, I always
     want it to be that way

865. Thirteen month old baby, broke the lookin' glass

866. That's when someone came up to me and said,
     young man take a walk up the street

867. Touched down in the land of the Delta Blues
     in the middle of the pouring rain

868. When I was young I never needed anyone

869. Here I lie in a lost and lonely part of town

870. I got my back against the record machine

871. Sinatra was swinging all the drunks they were singing

896. You could have told me yourself that you found someone else. Instead...

897. Although I might be laughing loud and hearty, deep inside I'm blue

898. I should have known better but I got what I deserved

899. A year has passed since I wrote my note

900. We hardly need to use our ears, how music changes through the years

901. I saw the rain dirty valley, you saw "Brigadoon"

902. Are you lonely just like me

903. Nothing more to say, no more ace to play

904. Look around you, all you see are sympathetic eyes

905. Let the words of our mouth and the meditation of our hearts

906. I know it's not much but it's the best I can do

907. You set your mark on stealing my heart away, crying, trying, anything for you

908. Well you're dirty and sweet , clad in black, don't look back, and I love you

909. 'Cause it doesn't make a difference if we make it or not

910. We've come too far to leave it all behind

911. And the wonder of it all is that you just don't realize

912. If your life was bad to you just think what tomorrow will do

913. I know it sounds absurd but please tell me who I am

914. Standin' on your mama's porch, you told me that you'd wait forever

915. When you leave I'm begging you not to go, call your name two, three times in a row

916. I met this fly girl in a club went by the name of Pecan deluxe

917. Well let the boys all sing and the boys all shout for tomorrow

918. And it hasn't been your day, your week, your month, or even your year

919. No matter where I go I`ll never find a better prize

944. So when I'm lying in my bed, thoughts running through my head

945. Only boys who save their pennies, make my rainy day

946. You can't tell me it's not worth dyin' for

947. But all the promises we make, from the cradle to the grave

948. So you run and you run to catch up with the sun but it's sinking

949. You should've seen by the look in my eyes, baby, there was somethin' missin'

950. Oh, I see a man at the back, as a matter of fact his eyes are red as the sun

951. When a man named Al Capone tried to make that town his own

952. She's really got a magical spell and it's working so well

953. The formula for Heaven's very simple, just follow the rules and you will see

954. We are young, heartache to heartache we stand

955. Mama put my guns in the ground

956. I should have changed my stupid lock, I should have made you leave your key

957. Life is a moment in space, when the dream is gone, It's a lonelier place

958. I've been waiting for this moment, all my life

959. She just can't be chained, to a life where nothing's gained

960. Lookin' for a lover who needs another, don't want another night on my own

961. I know every engineer on every train, all of their children, and all of their names

962. Take me on a trip upon your magic swirlin' ship

963. Goodbye my friend it's hard to die

964. Something's gotten into my life, cutting its way through my dreams like a knife

965. There ain't no more, you've taken everything

966. Closed the door and left me blinded by the light

967. Some people call me Maurice,

Name that Song!

993. Jubilation, she loves me again

994. I remember one Saturday night, we had fried fish and Johnny-cakes

995. You're giving love instinctively, round and round you're turning me

996. What'll you do when you get lonely, and nobody's waiting by your side

997. Better stop dreaming of the quiet life – cos it's the one we'll never know

998. And time goes by so slowly, and time can do so much

999. Just a man and his will to survive

1000. Get your act together we could be just fine

1001. Disappointment haunted all my dreams

Quiz 5

The Bonus Tracks
(Ditties from the Decades)

The Sixties

1002. I got a big fat mama trying to break me

1003. Wouldn't it be nice to get on with me neighbours

1004. I've been for a walk, on a winter's day

1005. We've got to get together sooner or later because the revolution's here

1006. That's when Billy would take me walking, through the back yard we'd go walking

1007. With all the charms of a woman, you've kept the secret of your youth

1008. We'd like to know a little bit about you, for our files

1009. No cigarettes, no sleep, no light, no sound, nothing to eat, no books to read

1010. So I asked to see her next week and she told

me I could

1011. Is she sleeping? I don't think so, is she breathing? Yes, very low.

1012. You're bringin' me down, you stood there and watched as, my baby left town

1013. The six o'clock alarm would never ring

1014. I hear footsteps slowly walking, as they gently walk across the lonely floor

1015. Woke up one morning half asleep, with all my blankets in a heap

1016. Grocer Jack, Grocer Jack, get off your back, go into town, don't let them down

1017. My makeup is dry and it cracks on my chin

1018. There's a five minute break and that's all you take

1019. They seek him here, they seek him there

1020. I can tell by the way you dress that you're so refined, ba ba ba ba

1021. It is written on the wind, that's everywhere I go

1022. So we sailed into the sun, 'till we found a sea

of green
1023. Then every guy will envy me, cause paradise is where I'll be

1024. At the end of a storm is a golden sky and the sweet, silver song of a lark

1025. Lemonade pie with a brand new car. Cantalope eyes come to me tonight

The Seventies

1026. She's really got a magical spell and it's working so well

1027. When the weather's fine we go fishing or go swimming in the sea

1028. And hear them echo through the hills "Ah, peace throughout the land"

1029. Did you ever read about a frog who dreamed of being a king
And then became one

1030. I had nothing to do on this hot afternoon but to settle down and write you a line

1031. We laugh, tell a few jokes but it still doesn't ease my pain

1032. I don't mean to sound degradin', but with a face like that you got nothin' to laugh about

1033. There's a rumour goin' round death row that a fuse is gonna blow

1034. When you come back, and you're beside me,

1035. I'm walking in the rain, chasing after rainbows I may never find again

1036. You've been laying it down, you've got your hip swinging out of bounds

1037.   The history book on the shelf is always repeating itself

1038.   Blue eyes, blue eyes, how can you tell so many lies?

1039.   See the mice in their million hordes, from Ibeza to the Norfolk Broads

1040.   She wanted to be Betty Grable but now she sits there at that beer stained table

1041.   Miles and miles of empty space in between us

1042.   Well we rolled up interstate forty-four like a rocket sled on rails

1043.   It's the only thing I've got, it's my piece of the rock

1044.   She moves through the light, controlling my mind and my soul

1045.   I saw your guy with a different girl looks like he's in another world

1046.   And don't come crying to me when you're the lonely one

1047.   More loneliness than any man could bear

1048.   So excuse me forgetting but these things I do

1049.   You make me sad with your eyes, you're telling me lies

The Eighties

1050. Everyone's a superhero, everyone's a Captain Kirk

1051. And the public gets what the public wants but I want nothing this society's got

1052. They got a message from the action man, I'm happy hope you're happy too

1053. No need for greed or hunger, a brotherhood of man

1054. I'm in the groove, babe, so get on up and let your body sway

1055. Get a run for your money and take a chance and it'll turn out right

1056. We're leaving together, but still it's farewell

1057. How many heartaches must I stand before I find the love to let me live again

1058. We can take it to the end of the line, your love is like a shadow on me all of the time

1059. You had romance, did you break it by chance over me

1060. And when she's walking, she's looking so fine

1061. Though it's easy to pretend, I know your not a fool

1062. Give me a melody, that's all that I ever need. The music is my salvation

1063. My knees are shakin' baby, my heart it beats like a drum

1064. I'm gonna lock her up in a trunk, so no big hunk, can steal her away from me

1065. Your started this fire down in my soul, now can you see it's burning out of control

1066. There's no life on earth, no other could see me through

1067. When the mountain was high, I still believed

1068. Something's gotten into my life, cutting its way through my dreams like a knife

1069. When all of my dreams are a heart beat away, and the answers are all up to me

1070. You give me one good reason to leave me, I' ll give you ten good reasons to stay

1071. Don't go for second best baby, put your love to the test

1072. I can hardly bear the sight of lipstick, on the cigarettes there in the ashtray

1073. Naughty boys in nasty schools, headmasters breaking all the rules

The Nineties

1074. If you know what it's like, to dream a dream, baby hold me tight and let this be

1075. Promises, promises turn to dust, wedding bells just turn to rust

1076. Honey, it's getting close to midnight and all the myths are still in town

1077. The world and I, we are still waiting, still hesitating

1078. Now I believe in miracles and a miracle has happened tonight

1079. Gal yuh fi jump an prance (Prowl off, jump an prance)

1080. It makes no difference if you're black or white, if you're a boy or a girl

1081. I'm the kid that made delinquency an art (last name Simpson, first name Bart)

1082. Sometimes I feel I'm gonna break down and cry (so lonely)

1083. But maybe you ain't never gonna feel this way you ain't never gonna know me but I know you

1084. You always smile but in your eyes your sorrow shows

1085. It's party time and not one minute we can lose, be my baby

1086. Oh don't leave me alone like this, don't you say it's the final kiss

1087. Whatever I said, whatever I did I didn't mean it

1088. Step outside the summertime's in bloom

1089. If you really bug me then I'll say goodbye

1090. She said, "I think I remember the film, and as I recall, I think we both kinda liked it"

1091. Mine's on the forty-five Mohammed Ruffi (forty-five) Lata Mangeshka (forty-five)

1092. Who can deny the joy it brings when you've found that special thing

1093. This world has lost it's glory, let's start a brand new story

1094. Life in plastic, it's fantastic, you can brush my hair

1095. Say you will say you won't say you'll do what I don't

1096. A little bit of Rita is all I need, A little bit of Tina is what I see

1097. You'll be so high you'll be flying

Beyond 2000 (The Noughties)

1098. It might seem like a crush but it doesn't mean that I'm serious

1099. But if you feel like I feel, I got the antedote, women wave your pantyhose, sing the chorus and it goes....

1100. You thought you'd found a friend, to take you out of this place

1101. Looking back on where we first met, I cannot escape and I cannot forget

1102. Never admit to a word weh she say, and if she claim a you tell her baby no way

1103. Don't stop movin' to the funky, funky beat

1104. Bob and the gang have so much fun, working together they get the job done

1105. Where the sound of the crowd, is so far away

1106. Instead of makin' me better, you keep makin' me ill

1107. Wanna fly to a place where it's just you and me, nobody else so we can be free

1108. Waters runnin' in the wrong direction, got a feelin' its a mixed up sign

1109.   Girl I wanna make you mine I want to be with a
        woman just like you

1110.   Hey now you're a Rock Star get the show on get paid,
        (And all that glitters is gold), Only shooting stars
        break the mold

Answers

Nice 'n' Easy from A–Z

1. 10CC – *I'm Not In Love*
2. AC-DC – *Moneytalks*
3. AC-DC – *Highway To Hell*
4. Paula Abdul – *Opposites Attract*
5. Bryan Adams – *Summer Of' 69*
6. Bryan Adams – *(Everything I Do) I Do It For You*
7. Christina Aguilera – *Come On Over (All I Want Is You)*
8. Christina Aguilera – *What A Girl Wants*
9. Christina Aguilera – *Beautiful*
10. AHA – *Take On Me*
11. America – *Horse With No Name*
12. Aqua – *Barbie Girl*
13. Louis Armstrong – *Wonderful World*
14. Ashanti – *Leaving (Always On Time)*
15. Rick Astley – *Never Gonna Give You Up*
16. Rick Astley – *Together Forever*
17. Charles Aznavour – *She*
18. B52's – *Love Shack*
19. The Animals – *House Of The Rising Sun*
20. ABBA – *Dancing Queen*
21. Bachman-Turner Overdrive – *Aint Seen Nothing Yet*
22. The Backstreet Boys – *I Want It That Way*
23. Joan Baez – *The Night They Drove Old Dixi Down*
24. Baha Men – *Who Let The Dogs Out*
25. Bananarama – *Venus*
26. Tony Basil – *Mickey*
27. Shirley Bassey – *Diamonds Are Forever*
28. The Beach Boys – *Help Me Rhonda*
29. The Beach Boys – *Good Vibrations*
30. Daniel Bedingfield – *Gotta Get Thru This*
31. Bee Gees – *Massachusetts*

32. Bee Gees – *Tragedy*
33. Harry Belafonte – *Mary's Boy Child*
34. Berlin – *Take My Breath Away*
35. Berry Chuck – *No Particular Place To Go*
36. Berry Chuck – *Roll Over Beethoven*
37. Acker Bilk (Andy Williams) – *Stranger on the Shore*
38. Mary J Blige – *As*
39. Blondie – *Heart Of Glass*
40. Blondie – *The Tide Is High*
41. Blues Brothers – *Everybody Needs Somebody*
42. Michael Bolton – *When A Man Loves A Woman*
43. Bon Jovi – *Bad Medicine*
44. Bon Jovi – *Livin' On A Prayer*
45. Jon Bon Jovi – *Blaze Of Glory*
46. David Bowie – *Ashes To Ashes*
47. David Bowie – *Let's Dance*
48. David Bowie – *Starman*
49. Boyz II Men – *One Sweet Day*
50. Brandy/ Monica – *The Boy Is Mine*
51. Toni Braxton – *Un-Break My Heart*
52. Bread – *Baby I'm-A Want You*
53. Bread – *The Guitar Man*
54. Garth Brooks – *The Dance*
55. Garth Brooks – *If Tomorrow Never Comes*
56. James Brown – *Living In America*
57. Jackson Browne – *Stay*
58. Kate Bush – *Wuthering Heights*
59. Buggles – *Video Killed The Radio Star*
60. The Byrds – *Mr. Tambourine Man*
61. Glen Campbell – *Rhinestone Cowboy*
62. Irene Cara – *Fame*
63. Irene Cara – *Flashdance... What A Feeling*
64. Belinda Carlisle – *Heaven Is A Place On Earth*
65. Nillson / Mariah Carey – *Without You*
66. The Cars – *Drive*
67. The Cars – *My Best Friend's Girl*
68. Johnny Cash – *A Boy Named Sue*
69. Johnny Cash – *Ring Of Fire*
70. David Cassidy – *Daydreamer*
71. Peter Cetera – *Glory Of Love*

72. Harry Chapin – *W.O.L.D.*
73. Tracy Chapman – *Fast Car*
74. Charlene – *I've Never Been To Me*
75. Ray Charles – *I Can't Stop Loving You*
76. Chubby Checker – *Let's Twist Again*
77. Cheeky Girls – *Cheeky Song (Touch My Bum)*
78. Cher – *Believe*
79. Chic – *Le Freak*
80. Chicago – *If You Leave Me Now*
81. Chicago – *Hard To Say I Sorry*
82. Eric Clapton – *I Shot The Sheriff*
83. Eric Clapton – *Tears In Heaven*
84. Eric Clapton – *Wonderful Tonight*
85. Petula Clark – *Downtown*
86. Dave Clark Five / Quiet Riot – *Glad All Over*
87. The Clash – *Should I Stay Or Should I Go*
88. Rosemary Clooney / Jimmy Dean / Shakin Stevens – *This Ole House*
89. Eddie Cochran – *C'mon Everybody*
90. Joe Cocker – *With A Little Help From My Friends*
91. Joe Cocker – *Up Where We Belong*
92. Natalie Cole – *Miss You Like Crazy*
93. Phil Collins – *Against All Odds*
94. Phil Collins – *You Can't Hurry Love*
95. Perry Como – *Magic Moments*
96. Perry Como – *For The Good Times*
97. Sam Cooke – *Wonderful World*
98. Coolio – *Gangsta's Paradise*
99. Madonna / Julie Covington (Others) – *Don't Cry For Me Argentina*
100. The Cranberries – *Promises*
101. The Corrs – *Breathless*
102. Creedence Clearwater Revival – *Bad Moon Rising*
103. Creedence Clearwater Revival – *Proud Mary*
104. Sheryl Crow – *All I Wanna Do*
105. Beyonce – *Crazy In Love*
106. Destiny's Child – *Say My Name*
107. Cutting Crew – *(I Just) Died In Your Arms*
108. The Dandy Warhols – *Bohemian Like You*
109. Terence Trent D'arby – *Wishing Well*

110. Bobby Goldsboro / Bobby Darin – *Honey*
111. Dawn – *Knock Three Times*
112. Tony Orlando & Dawn – *Tie A Yellow Ribbon*
113. Chris DeBurgh – *Lady In Red*
114. Elton John & Kiki Dee – *Don't Go Breaking My Heart*
115. Bobby Darin / Frank Sinatra / Robbie Williams – *Mack The Knife*
116. Deep Purple – *Black Night*
117. Desmond Dekker And The Aces – *Israelites*
118. Destiny's Child – *Say My Name*
119. Detroit Spinners / Boyzone – *Working My Way Back To You*
120. Dexy's Midnight Runners – *Come On Eileen*
121. Celine Dion – *The Power Of Love*
122. Dire Straits – *Money For Nothing*
123. Dire Straits – *Sultans Of Swing*
124. Dr. Hook & The Medicine Show – *When You're In Love With A Beautiful Woman*
125. Fats Domino – *Ain't That A Shame*
126. Doobie Brothers – *Listen To The Music*
127. The Doors – *Light My Fire*
128. Carl Douglas / Wang Chung – *Kung Fu Fighting*
129. The Drifters – *Save The Last Dance For Me*
130. The Drifters – *There Goes My First Love*
131. Duran Duran – *The Reflex*
132. Bob Dylan – *The Times They Are A-Changin'*
133. Bob Dylan – *Blowin' In The Wind*
134. Bob Dylan – *Baby Stop Crying*
135. Electric Light Orchestra – *Don't Bring Me Down*
136. Enya – *Orinoco Flow*
137. Erasure – *Sometimes*
138. Gloria Estefan – *Here We Are*
139. Eurythmics – *Sweet Dreams Are Made Of This*
140. Everly Brothers – *Bye Bye Love*
141. Everly Brothers – *Cathy's Clown*
142. Exile – *Kiss You All Over*
143. Falco – *Rock Me Amadeus*
144. Fine Young Cannibals – *She Drives Me Crazy*
145. Aretha Franklin / Roberta Flack / The Fugees – *Killing Me Softly*

146. Fleetwood Mac – *Everywhere*
147. Foreigner – *I Want To Know What Love Is*
148. Foo Fighters – *All My Life*
149. 4 Non Blondes – *What's Up*
150. Four Seasons – *December 1963 – Oh What A Night*
151. The Four Tops – *Reach Out I'll Be There*
152. Frankie Goes To Hollywood – *Relax*
153. Aretha Franklin & George Michael – *I Knew You Were Waiting*
154. Dean Friedman – *Lucky Stars*
155. Peter Gabriel – *Sledgehammer*
156. Art Garfunkel – *Bright Eyes*
157. Marvin Gaye – *I Heard It Through The Grapevine*
158. Gloria Gaynor – *I Will Survive*
159. J Geils Band – *Centerfold*
160. Gibson Brothers – *Que Sera Ma Vida – (If You Should Go)*
161. Andrew Gold – *Never Let Her Slip Away*
162. Eddy Grant – *Electric Avenue*
163. Bob Dylan / Guns 'N' Roses – *Knockin' On Heavens Door*
164. Adrian Gurvitz – *Classic*
165. Hall & Oates – *Maneater*
166. MC Hammer – *U Can't Touch This*
167. Albert Hammond – *Free Electric Band*
168. Richard Harris / Donna Summer – *Macarthur Park*
169. George Harrison – *My Sweet Lord*
170. George Harrison – *Got My Mind Set On You*
171. Jimi Hendrix – *Purple Haze*
172. The Hollies – *He Ain't Heavy He's My Brother*
173. Kris Kristofferson / Elvis Presley / John Holt – *Help Me Make It Through The Night*
174. Thelma Houston – *Don't Leave Me This Way*
175. Whitney Houston – *I Will Always Love You*
176. Whitney Houston – *How Will I Know*
177. Hues Corporation – *Rock The Boat*
178. Human League – *Don't You Want Me*
179. Brian Hyland – *Itsy Bitsy Teenie Weenie Yellow Polka Dot Bikini*
180. Billy Idol – *White Wedding*
181. Terry Jacks / Westlife – *Seasons In The Sun*

182. Janet Jackson – *Together Again*
183. Michael Jackson – *Smooth Criminal*
184. Michael Jackson – *Wanna Be Startin' Somethin'*
185. Michael Jackson – *Rockin' Robin*
186. The Jam – *Town Called Malice*
187. Jesus And Mary Chain – *April Skies*
188. Joan Jett – *I Love Rock ' N' Roll*
189. Billy Joel – *We Didn't Start The Fire*
190. Elton John – *Don't Let The Sun Go Down On Me*
191. Elton John – *Rocket Man*
192. Elton John – *Saturday Night's Alright For Fighting*
193. Grace Jones – *Pull Up To The Bumper Baby*
194. KC and The Sunshine Band – *That's The Way (I Like It)*
195. Katrina And The Waves – *Walking On Sunshine*
196. R Kelly & Celine Dion – *I'm Your Angel*
197. Chaka Khan – *I Feel For You*
198. BB King & U2 – *When Love Comes To Town*
199. Andy Kim – *Rock Me Gently*
200. Ben E King – *Stand By Me*
201. The Kinks – *Sunny Afternoon*
202. The Knack – *My Sharona*
203. Gladys Knight & The Pips – *Midnight Train To Georgia*
204. Kool And The Gang – *Celebration*
205. LL Cool J – *Ain't Nobody*
206. Greg Lake – *I Believe In Father Christmas*
207. Denise Lasalle – *My Toot Toot*
208. Las Ketchup – *The Ketchup Song (Asereje)*
209. Cyndi Lauper – *True Colors*
210. John Lennon – *Imagine*
211. John Lennon – *Woman*
212. Jerry Lee Lewis – *Great Balls Of Fire*
213. Huey Lewis And The News – *The Power Of Love*
214. Lipps Inc – *Funkytown*
215. Little Richard – *Good Golly Miss Molly*
216. Lobo – *Me And You And A Dog Named Boo*
217. Kenny Loggins – *Footloose*
218. J-Lo (Jennifer Lopez) – *Jenny From The Block*
219. Los Lobos – *La Bamba*
220. Los Del Rio – *Macarena*

221. Lynyrd Skynyrd – *Sweet Home Alabama*
222. M – *Pop Muzik*
223. Paul McCartney – *Band On The Run*
224. Paul McCartney – *Ebony And Ivory*
225. Paul McCartney – *Listen To What The Man Said*
226. Marilyn McCoo & Billy Davis Jr – *You Don't Have To Be A Star*
227. Van McCoy – *The Hustle*
228. George McCrae – *Rock Your Baby*
229. McFadden & Whitehead – *Ain't No Stopping Us Now*
230. Bobby McFerrin – *Don't Worry Be Happy*
231. Maria McKee – *Show Me Heaven*
232. Scott McKenzie – *San Francisco*
233. Don McLean – *Vincent*
234. Mamas And Papas – *Monday Monday*
235. Manfred Mann – *Do Wah Diddy Diddy*
236. Barry Manilow – *Mandy*
237. Barry Manilow – *Copacabana*
238. Bob Marley – *Buffalo Soldier*
239. Bob Marley – *No Woman No Cry*
240. Lena Martell – *One Day At A Time*
241. Dean Martin – *Memories Are Made Of This*
242. Dean Martin – *That's Amore*
243. Ricky Martin – *Livin' La Vida Loca*
244. Theme From Mash – *Suicide Is Painless*
245. Meat Loaf – *Bat Out Of Hell*
246. Meat Loaf – *Two Out Of Three Ain't Bad*
247. Men at Work – *Down Under*
248. Gloria Estefan & Miami Sound Machine – *Anything For You*
249. George Michael – *Careless Whisper*
250. George Michael – *Faith*
251. Bette Midler – *Wind Beneath My Wings*
252. Mike & The Mechanics – *The Living Years*
253. John Miles – *Music*
254. Steve Miller Band – *Abracadabra*
255. Steve Miller Band – *The Joker*
256. Kylie Minogue – *Can't Get You Out Of My Head*
257. Joni Mitchell – *Big Yellow Taxi*
258. Smokey Robinson & The Miracles – *Tears Of A Clown*

259. The Monkees – *Daydream Believer*
260. The Monkees – *I'm A Believer*
261. The Moody Blues – *Nights In White Satin*
262. Philip Oakey And Giorgio Moroder – *Together In Electric Dreams*
263. The Muppet Show Theme
264. Allanah Myles – *Black Velvet*
265. Johnny Nash – *I Can See Clearly Now*
266. Nelly, Kelly Rowland – *Dilemma*
267. Elvis Presley / Willie Nelson – *Always On My Mind*
268. New Kids On The Block – *Step By Step*
269. John Travolta / Olivia Newton-John – *Summer Nights*
270. Nickleback – *How You Remind Me*
271. Nilsson – *Without You*
272. Notorious B.I.G. featuring Mase, Puff Daddy – *Mo Money Mo Problems*
273. Gary Numan – *Are' Friends' Electric?*
274. Billy Ocean – *When The Going Get Tough*
275. Sinead O'Connor – *Nothing Compares To You*
276. The O'Jays – *Love Train*
277. (The Police) Puff Daddy & Faith Evans Featuring 112 – *I'll Be Missing You*
278. Roy Orbison – *Oh Pretty Woman*
279. OMD – *Joan Of Arc (Maid Of Orleans)*
280. Donny Osmond – *The Twelfth Of Never*
281. The Osmonds – *Love Me For A Reason*
282. Gilbert O'Sullivan – *Claire*
283. Ottawan – *D.I.S.C.O.*
284. Ottawan – *Hands Up*
285. Patti Page – *The Doggie In The Window (1953)*
286. Robert Palmer – *Addicted To Love*
287. Paper Lace – *The Night Chicago Died*
288. John Parr – *St. Elmo's Fire*
289. Dolly Parton & Kenny Rogers – *Islands In The Stream*
290. The Partridge Family – *I Think I Love You*
291. Pet Shop Boys – *West End Girls*
292. Peter, Paul & Mary – *Leaving On A Jet Plane*
293. Pink – *Just Like A Pill*
294. Gene Pitney – *Something`S Gotten Hold Of My Heart*
295. Pointer Sisters – *Jump*

296. Sting & Police – *Every Breath You Take*
297. Prince – *1999*
298. Prince – *Purple Rain*
299. Roger Millar / Proclaimers / Others – *King Of The Road*
300. Procol Harum – *Whiter Shade Of Pale*
301. Queen – *Another One Bites The Dust*
302. Queen – *Crazy Little Thing Called Love*
303. Queen – *We Are The Champions*
304. R.E.M. – *Everybody Hurts*
305. R.E.M. – *Losing My Religion*
306. Reo Speedwagon – *Keep On Loving You*
307. Ram Jam – *Black Betty*
308. The Ramones – *Baby I Love You*
309. Red Hot Chili Peppers – *By The Way*
310. Otis Redding – *Sitting On The Dock Of The Bay Lyrics*
311. Helen Reddy – *Angie Baby*
312. Lou Reed – *Walk On The Wild Side*
313. Martha Reeves & The Vandellas (1964), Mick Jagger / David Bowie – *Dancing In The Street*
314. Charlie Rich – *The Most Beautiful Girl*
315. Cliff Richard – *Living Doll*
316. Cliff Richard – *Saviour's Day*
317. Lionel Richie – *All Night Long*
318. Lionel Richie – *Hello*
319. The Righteous Brothers (And Many Others) – *Unchained Melody*
320. Right Said Fred – *I'm Too Sexy*
321. Righteous Brothers – *You've Lost That Lovin' Feelin'*
322. Kenny Rogers & Sheena Easton – *We've Got Tonight*
323. Diana Ross – *Chain Reaction*
324. Roxette – *Joyride*
325. Roxette – *The Look*
326. Run D.M.C. & Aerosmith – *Walk This Way*
327. Jennifer Rush – *The Power Of Love*
328. Sade – *Your Love Is King*
329. Peter Sarstedt – *Where Do You Go To My Lovely*
330. Telly Savalas – *If*
331. Leo Sayer – *When I Need You*
332. Boz Scaggs – *Lido Shuffle*
333. Seal – *Kiss From A Rose*

334. Neil Sedaka – *Laughter In The Rain*
335. Bob Seger – *We've Got Tonight*
336. Tom Jones – *Delilah*
337. Shaggy – *It Wasn't Me*
338. Del Shannon – *Runaway*
339. Shangri-Las – *Leader Of The Pack*
340. Labi Siffre – *Something Inside So Strong*
341. Carly Simon – *You're So Vain*
342. Paul Simon – *50 Ways To Leave Your Lover*
343. Simon & Garfunkel – *The Boxer*
344. Simon & Garfunkel – *Mrs. Robinson*
345. Simple Minds – *Don't You (Forget About Me)*
346. Simply Red – *If You Don't Know Me By Now*
347. Frank Sinatra – *I've Got You Under My Skin*
348. Frank & Nancy Sinatra – *Something Stupid*
349. Gene Kelly – *Singing In The Rain*
350. Percy Sledge – *When A Man Loves A Woman*
351. Will Smith – *Wild Wild West*
352. Sonny & Cher – *I Got You Babe*
353. David Soul – *Don't Give Up On Us*
354. Sutherland Brothers And Quiver – *Lyin' In The Arms Of Mary*
355. Sparks – *This Town Ain't Big Enough For Both Of Us*
356. Britney Spears – *Baby One More Time Lyrics*
357. The Spice Girls – *Wannabe*
358. Rick Springfield – *Jessie's Girl*
359. Bruce Springsteen – *Born To Run*
360. Bruce Springsteen – *Dancing In The Dark*
361. Bruce Springsteen – *Born In The Usa*
362. Lisa Stansfield – *All Around The World*
363. Ringo Starr – *You're Sixteen*
364. Starship – *We Built This City*
365. Candi Staton – *Nights On Broadway*
366. Steely Dan – *Reeling In The Years*
367. Cat Stevens – *Moon Shadow*
368. Ray Stevens – *The Streak*
369. Ami Stewart – *Knock On Wood*
370. Rod Stewart – *Tonight's The Night*
371. Rod Stewart – *The First Cut Is The Deepest*

372. Rod Stewart – *You're In My Heart*
373. The Stranglers – *Golden Brown*
374. The Stray Cats – *Runaway Boys*
375. Barbara Streisand – *Woman In Love*
376. Barbara Streisand – *The Rose*
377. Styx – *Babe*
378. Donna Summer – *Hot Stuff*
379. Supertramp – *Logical Song*
380. Billy Swan – *I Can Help*
381. Marc Bolan & T-Rex – *Get It On*
382. Talking Heads – *Road To Nowhere*
383. James Taylor – *You've Got A Friend*
384. Tears For Fears – *Shout*
385. The Temptations – *My Girl*
386. B.J. Thomas – *Raindrops Keep Fallin' On My Head*
387. Three Degrees – *When Will I See You Again*
388. Tiffany – *I Think We're Alone Now*
389. Toto – *Africa*
390. The Traveling Wilburys – *End Of The Line*
391. John Travolta / Olivia Newton John – *Summer Nights*
392. The Troggs – *Wild Thing*
393. Trio – *Da Da Da*
394. Ike & Tina Turner – *Nutbush City Limits*
395. Tina Turner – *Private Dancer*
396. Tina Turner – *The Best*
397. Shania Twain – *That Don't Impress Me Much*
398. Conway Twitty, The Hollies, Glen Campbell – *It's Only Make Believe*
399. Bonnie Tyler – *Total Eclipse Of The Heart*
400. UB40 & Chrissie Hynde – *I Got You Babe*
401. Ultravox – *Vienna*
402. USA For Africa – *We Are The World*
403. Band Aid – *Feed The World*
404. Van Halen – *Jump*
405. Van Morrison – *Bright Side Of The Road*
406. The Vapors – *Turning Japanese*
407. Susanne Vega – *Marlene On The Wall*
408. Village People – *In The Navy*
409. Village People – *Y.M.C.A.*
410. Joe Cocker & Jennifer Warnes – *Up Where We Belong*

411. Dionne Warwick – *Heartbreaker*
412. Weather Girls – *It's Raining Men*
413. Wet Wet Wet – *Sweet Little Mystery*
414. Wham – *Wake Me Up Before You Go Go*
415. Wham – *Last Christmas*
416. Whigfield – *Saturday Night*
417. Barry White – *You're The First, The Last, My Everything*
418. Whitesnake – *Here I Go Again*
419. The Who / Elton John – *Pinball Wizard*
420. Wild Cherry – *Play That Funky Music*
421. Kim Wilde – *Keep Me Hanging On*
422. Andy Williams – *Cant' Take My Eyes Off You*
423. Bruce Willis / Drifters / Others – *Under The Boardwalk*
424. Jackie Wilson – *Reet Petite*
425. Bill Withers – *Lean On Me*
426. Stevie Wonder – *Superstition*
427. Tammy Wynette – *Stand By Your Man*
428. Neil Young – *Heart Of Gold*
429. Paul Young – *Everytime You Go Away*
430. Sydney Youngblood – *If Only I Could*
431. ZZ Top – *Gimme All Your Lovin'*
432. ZZ Top – *Sharp Dressed Man*

Lines Back to Back

433. *Bette Davis Eyes* – Kim Carnes
434. *Bohemian Rhapsody* – Queen
435. *Seven Spanish Angels* – Ray Charles / Willie Nelson
436. *Let's Dance* – David Bowie
437. *Don't You Want Me* – The Human League
438. *Imagine* – John Lennon
439. *Maggie May* – Rod Stewart
440. *Schools Out* – Alice Cooper
441. *Bridge Over Troubled Water* – Simon & Garfunkel
442. *All Night Long* – Lionel Richie
443. *Riders on the Storm* – The Doors
444. *Down Under* – Men At Work
445. *My Girl* – The Temptations
446. *All Right Now* – Free

447. *West End Girls* – The Pet Shop Boys
448. *The Green Green Grass of Home* – Tom Jones
449. *Back for Good* – Take That
450. *Puff The Magic Dragon* – Peter, Paul and Mary
451. *Heart of Glass* – Blondie
452. *Satisfaction* – The Rolling Stones
453. *Eight Days A Week* – The Beatles
454. *I've Got You Babe* – Sonny & Cher
455. *I Am A Rock* – Simon & Garfunkel
456. *In The Ghetto* – Elvis Presley
457. *In The Air Tonight* – Phil Collins
458. *New Years Day* – U2
459. *Once in a Lifetime* – Talking Heads
460. *Use It Up And Wear It Out* – Odyssey
461. *Who Are You* – The Who
462. *The Jean Genie* – David Bowie
463. *Big Yellow Taxi* – Joni Mitchell
464. *She's Alwaya A Woman* – Billy Joel
465. *The Logical Song* – Supertramp
466. *We Can Work It Out* – The Beatles
467. *Like A Prayer* – Madonna
468. *Hotel California* – The Eagles
469. *Waterloo* – ABBA
470. *Beat It* – Michael Jackson
471. *Nothing Compares 2U* – Sinead O'Connor
472. *I'll Be Your Baby Tonight* – Bob Dylan, Robert Plamer or UB40
473. *Night Moves* – Bob Seger
474. *Space Oddity* – David Bowie
475. *Rock' n Roll (I gave you all the best years of my life)* – Kevin Johnson
476. *Fire and Rain* – James Taylor
477. *Annie's Song* – John Denver
478. *(They Long To Be) Close To You* – The Carpenters / Andy Williams
479. *Wichita Linesman* – Glen Campbell
480. *A Hard Day's Night* – The Beatles
481. *Let Your Love Flow* – Bellamy Brothers
482. *Everything I Own* – Ken Booth
483. *Rhinestone Cowboy* – Glen Campbell

484. *Yesterday Once More* – The Carpenters
485. *If You Leave Me Now* – Chicago
486. *Amazing Grace* – Judy Collins
487. *Bad, Bad Leroy Brown* – Jim Croce
488. *Cracklin' Rosie* – Neil Diamond
489. *Billy Don't Be A Hero* – Bo Donaldson (US) Paper Lace (UK)
490. *You Don't Bring Me Flowers* – Barbara Streisand and Neil Diamond
491. *Killing Me Softly With His Song* – Roberta Flack
492. *Don't It Make My Brown Eyes Blue* – Crystal Gayle
493. *Jump* – Van Halen
494. *With or Without You* – U2
495. *Dancing In The Dark* – Bruce Springsteen
496. *Don't You (Forget About Me)* – Simple Minds
497. *I Still Haven't Found What I'm Looking For* – U2
498. *Keep on Loving You* – REO Speedwagon
499. *It Never Rains in Southern California* – Albert Hammond
500. *He Ain't Heavy, He's My Brother* – Neil Diamond / The Hollies
501. *Goodbye Yellow Brick Road* – Elton John
502. *Sundown* – Gordon Lightfoot
503. *Copacabana (At the Copa)* – Barry Manilow
504. *Band On The Run* – Paul McCartney & Wings
505. *Radio Ga Ga* – Queen
506. *Every Breath You Take* – The Police
507. *Addicted To Love* – Robert Palmer
508. *Abracadabra* – The Steve Miller Band
509. *The Power of Love* – Huey Lewis & The News
510. *I Want To Know What Love Is* – Foreigner
511. *American Pie* – Don McLean
512. *You're the One That I Want* – Olivia Newton-John and John Travolta
513. *Tie A Yellow Ribbon Round The Ole Oak Tree* – Dawn / Tony Orlando
514. *Lucille* – Kenny Rogers
515. *You're So Vain* – Carly Simon
516. *The Way We Were* – Barbra Streisand
517. *Money for Nothing* – Dire Straits
518. *Dancing In The Streets* – David Bowie and Mick Jagger

519. *Livin' on a Prayer* – Bon Jovi
520. *Summer of' 69* – Bryan Adams
521. *If You Don't Know Me By Now* – Simply Red
522. *The Locomotion* – Kylie Minogue
523. *Raindrops Keep Fallin' On My Head* – B.J. Thomas
524. *Night Fever* – The Bee Gees
525. *Three Times A Lady* – The Commodores
526. *I Will Survive* – Gloria Gaynor
527. *You Sexy Thing* – Hot Chocolate
528. *Midnight Train to Georgia* – Gladys Knight & The Pips
529. *The Best* – Tina Turner
530. *Never Gonna Give You Up* – Rick Astley
531. *Come On Eileen* – Dexys Midnight Runners
532. *Celebration* – Kool & the Gang
533. *Time After Time* – Cyndi Lauper
534. *Ebony And Ivory* – Paul McCartney / Stevie Wonder
535. *Rock the Boat* – The Hues Corporation
536. *I Can See Clearly Now* – Johnny Nash
537. *MacArthur Park* – Richard Harris
538. *Y.M.C.A.* – Village People
539. *You're The First, My Last, My Everything* – Barry White
540. *A Horse With No Name* – America
541. *Leader Of The Band* – Dan Fogelberg
542. *Papa Don't Preach* – Madonna
543. *Faith* – George Michael
544. *The Rose* – Bette Midler
545. *Always On My Mind* – Willie Nelson / Elvis
546. *Hello* – Lionel Richie
547. *You Ain't Seen Nothing Yet* – Bachman-Turner Overdrive
548. *More Than A Feeling* – Boston
549. *Stay* – Jackson Browne
550. *Cats In The Cradle* – Harry & Sandy Chapin
551. *Wonderful Tonight* – Eric Clapton
552. *Sultans Of Swing* – Dire Straits
553. *The Shoop Shoop Song* – Cher
554. *The Power Of Love* – Celine Dion
555. *I Will Always Love You* – Whitney Houston
556. *The River Of Dreams* – Billy Joel
557. *Candle In The Wind / England's Rose* – Elton John

558. *Don't Cry for Me Argentina* – Madonna (1997)
559. *When You're In Love With A Beautiful Woman* – Dr Hook
560. *Don't Stop* – Fleetwood Mac
561. *Free Bird* – Lynyrd Skynyrd
562. *Two Out Of Three Ain't Bad* – Meat Loaf
563. *The Joker* – The Steve Miller Band
564. *Nights In White Satin* – Moody Blues
565. *Don't Let the Sun Go Down On Me* – Elton John / George Michael
566. *It Must Have Been Love* – Roxette
567. *You're Still The One* – Shania Twain
568. *Summertime* – Sam Cooke
569. *Unforgettable* – Nat King Cole
570. *Total Eclipse Of The Heart* – Bonnie Tyler
571. *Enrique Iglesias* – Hero
572. *Elevation* – U2
573. *Nickelback* – How You Remind Me
574. *Whereever Whereever* – Shakira
575. *Rock DJ* – Robbie Williams
576. *No Woman No Cry* – Bob Marley
577. *The Wonder of You* – Elvis Presley
578. *Brown Sugar* – The Rolling Stones
579. *Born To Run* – Bruce Springsteen
580. *Manic Monday* – The Bangles
581. *Flashdance...What a Feeling* – Irene Cara
582. *If I Could Turn Back Time* – Cher
583. *Up Where We Belong* – Joe Cocker & Jennifer Warnes
584. *Ride Like The Wind* – Christopher Cross
585. *Karma Chameleon* – Culture Club
586. *Macarena* – Los Del Rio
587. *U Can't Touch This* – M.C. Hammer
588. *Cotton Eye Joe* – Rednex
589. *Baby One More Time* – Britney Spears
590. *Wannabe* – Spice Girls
591. *Save The Best For Last* – Vanessa Williams
592. *Everything I Do (I Do It For You)* – Bryan Adams
593. *Blaze Of Glory* – Jon Bon Jovi
594. *Layla Eric* – Clapton
595. *All I Wanna Do* – Sheryl Crow

596. *The Boys Are Back In Town* – Thin Lizzy / Everclear
597. *What's Going On* – 4 Non Blondes
598. *Suicide Blonde* – INXS
599. *I'd Do Anything For Love (But I Wont Do That)* – Meatloaf
600. *Wonderwall* – Oasis
601. *I'm Gonna Be (500 miles)* – The Proclaimers
602. *Everybody Hurts* – REM
603. *Fields Of Gold* – Sting
604. *Mysterious Ways* – U2
605. *Losing My Religion* – REM
606. *A Boy Named Sue* – Johnny Cash
607. *Dirrty* – Christina Aguilera
608. *Complicated* – Avril Lavigne
609. *Cry Me A River* – Justin Timberlake
610. *Take On Me* – A-Ha
611. *Hotel California* – The Eagles
612. *Good Vibrations* – The Beach Boys
613. *I Want To Know What Love Is* – Foreigner
614. *Hey Joe* – Jimi Hendrix
615. *Can't Get You Out Of My Head* – Kylie Minogue
616. T*hat's Amore* – Dean Martin
617. *Theme from M*A*S*H*
618. *Material World* – Madonna
619. *Only The Lonely* – Roy Orbison
620. *The Ketchup Song* – Las Ketchup
621. *Jenny From The Block* – Jennifer Lopez
622. *Seasons in the Sun* – Terry Jacks / Westlife
623. *Year of the Cat* – Al Stewart
624. *1999* – Prince
625. *Stayin' Alive* – The Bee Gees
626. *Hey Jude* – The Beatles
627. *Red Red Wine* – Neil Diamond
628. *Cabaret* – (musical)
629. *Eternal Flame* – The Bangles
630. *Summertime* – George Gershwin
631. *Highway To Hell* – AC/DC
632. *Stand and Deliver* – Adam Ant
633. *House of the Rising Sun* – The Animals
634. *Moon River* – Andy Williams

635. *Can't Smile Without You* – Barry Manilow
636. *Surfin' USA* – The Beach Boys
637. *Baby Stop Crying* – Bob Dylan
638. *Heaven Is A Place On Earth* – Belinda Carlisle
639. *Man! I Feel Like A Woman* – Shania Twain
640. *Bring It All Back* – S Club 7
641. *Smooth Operator* – Sade
642. *True* – Spandau Ballet
643. *Rikki Don't Lose That Number* – Steely Dan
644. *Come Fly With Me* – Frank Sinatra
645. *The Chain* – Fleetwood Mac
646. *Love Is A Battlefield* – Pat Benatar
647. *Crazy* – Patsy Cline / Willie Nelson
648. *Wonderful Christmastime* – Paul McCartney & Wings
649. *Sledgehammer* – Peter Gabriel
650. *And I Love You So* – Perry Como
651. *West End Girls* – The Pet Shop Boys
652. *Jealous Guy* – Bryan Ferry / Roxy Music
653. *Purple Rain* – Prince
654. *Tonight's The Night* – Rod Stewart
655. *Let Me Entertain You* – Robbie Williams
656. *Vincent* – Don McLean
657. *Money For Nothing* – Dire Straits
658. *Maneater* – Hall & Oates
659. *9 To 5* – Dolly Parton
660. *Smoke On The Water* – Deep Purple
661. *All By Myself* – Eric Carmen
662. *Roll Over Beethoven* – Electric Light Orchestra
663. *Pinball Wizard* – The Who
664. *Love is All Around* – Wet Wet Wet
665. *Lola* – The Kinks
666. *One In A Lifetime* – Talking Heads
667. *Delilah* – Tom Jones
668. *The Way You Do The Things You Do* – The Temptations
669. *Africa* – Toto
670. *Me And Bobby Magee* – Kris Kristofferson
671. *Kids in America* – Kim Wilde
672. *Wuthering Heights* – Kate Bush
673. *Up Where We Belong* – Joe Cocker
674. *I Love Rock' N Roll* – Joan Jett and The Blackhearts

675. *Cars* – Gary Numan
676. *Bad Moon Rising* – Creedence Clearwater Revival
677. *Claire* – Gilbert O'Sullivan
678. *Coward of The County* – Kenny Rogers
679. *Bright Eyes* – Art Garfunkel
680. *Rock Me Gently* – Andy Kim
681. *Walking on Broken Glass* – Annie Lennox
682. *Big in Japan* – Alphaville
683. *Weak In The Presence Of Beauty* – Alison Moyet
684. *Only The Lonely* – Roy Orbison
685. *It Never Rains In Southern California* – Albert Hammond
686. *Stand And Deliver* – Adam & The Ants
687. *Happy Birthday* – Altered Images
688. *The Young Ones* – Cliff Richard
689. *Yes Sir (I Can Boogie)* – Baccara
690. *Take These Chains From My Heart* – Ray Charles
691. *Give A Little Love* – Bay City Rollers
692. *Who Let The Dogs Out* – Baha Men
693. *The Night They Drove Old Dixie Down* – The Band
694. *The Way We Were* – Barbara Streisand
695. *You're The First* – Barry White
696. *Soul Man* – Blues Brothers
697. *Video Killed The Radio Star* – The Buggles
698. *Rock Around The Clock* – Bill Haley
699. *Top Of The World* – The Carpenters
700. *Drive* – The Cars
701. *Moonshadow* – Cat Stevens
702. *Dirrty* – Christina Aguilera
703. *If I Could Turn Back Time* – Cher
704. *Linger* – The Cranberries
705. *Johnny B. Goode* – Chuck Berry
706. *Three Times A Lady* – The Commodores
707. *Ride Like The Wind* – Christopher Cross
708. *Living Next Door To Alice* – Smokie
709. *I'm Into Something Good* – Hermans Hermits
710. *" Do you Know Where You're Going to"* (Theme From Mahogany) – Diana Ross
711. *Romeo & Juliet* – Dire Straits
712. *Under The Boardwalk* – The Drifters
713. *Riders on the Storm* – The Doors

Name that Song!

714. *Hot Stuff* – Donna Summer
715. *Strangers In The Night* – Frank Sinatra
716. *Let's Dance* – David Bowie
717. *Hungry Like The Wolf* – Duran Duran
718. *Listen to the Music* – Doobie Brothers
719. *Stairway to Heaven* – Led Zepplin
720. *Stayin' Alive* – The Bee Gees

Great Artists, Great Hits

One Line Intros
721. *Only You* – Yazoo / Flying Pickets
722. *Karma Chameleon* – Culture Club
723. *Whole Lotta Love* – Led Zepplin
724. *Wonderful Tonight* – Eric Clapton
725. *Girls Just Wanna Have Fun* – Cyndi Lauper
726. *Lovely Day* – Bill Withers
727. *Silenece is Golden* – The Tremeloes
728. *Mistletoe and Wine* – Cliff Richard
729. *Born To Run* – Bruce Springsteen
730. *Brown Sugar* – The Rolling Stones

One Hit Wonders
731. *Sometimes When We Touch* – Dan Hill
732. *All Right Now* – Free
733. *Wanderin' Star* – Lee Marvin
734. *It's Raining Men* – The Weather Girls
735. *Turning Japanese* – The Vapors
736. *Kung Fu Fighting* – Carl Douglas
737. *Convoy* – C.W. McCall
738. *99 Red Balloons* – Nena
739. *Don't Worry, Be Happy* – Bobby McFerrin
740. *Puttin' On The Ritz* – Taco

Elvis Presley
741. *A Little Less Conversation*
742. *Don't Be Cruel*
743. *I'm All Shook Up*
744. *Always On My Mind*

745. *Hound Dog*
746. *An American Trilogy*
747. *Jailhouse Rock*
748. *Are You Lonesome Tonight?*
749. *Love Me Tender*
750. *Blue Suede Shoes*
751. *Promised Land*
752. *Burning Love*
753. *That's All Right Mama*
754. *Always On My Mind*
755. *Don't Be Cruel*

The Beatles
756. *A Little Help From My Friends*
757. *All You Need Is Love*
758. *Back in the USSR*
759. *I Am The Walrus*
760. *Lady Madonna*
761. *Strawberry Fields Forever*
762. *Yesterday*
763. *Get Back*
764. *Can't Buy Me Love*
765. *Eleanor Rigby*

The Rolling Stones
766. *Angie*
767. *Brown Sugar*
768. *Honky Tonk Woman*
769. *It's Only Rock N Roll (But I Like It)*
770. *Route 66*
771. *Ruby Tuesday*
772. *Start Me Up*
773. *Tumbling Dice*
774. *Fool To Cry*
775. *Jumpin' Jack Flash*

Madonna
776. *Express Yourself*
777. *Holiday*
778. *Into The Groove*

779. *Like A Prayer*
780. *La Isla Bonita*
781. *Material Girl*
782. *Papa Don't Preach*
783. *Vogue*

The Eagles
784. *Best of My Love*
785. *Hotel California*
786. *Lyin' Eyes*
787. *One of These Nights*
788. *Peaceful Easy Feeling*
789. *Take It To The Limit*
790. *Tequila Sunrise*

U2
791. *Angel of Harlem*
792. *Beautiful Day*
793. *Elevation*
794. *I Will Follow*
795. *New Years Day*
796. *Pride (In the Name of Love)*
797. *The Sweetest Thing*
798. *Where the Streets Have no Name*
799. *All I Want Is You*
800. *Bad*

Musicals & Soundtracks
801. *Don't Cry For Me Argentina* – Evita
802. *A Spoonful of Sugar* – Mary Poppins
803. *Get Me to the Church on Time* – My Fair Lady
804. *The Candy Man* – Willy Wonka and the Chocolate Factory
805. *More Than A Woman (Tavares)* – Saturday Night Fever
806. *Edelweiss* – The Sound Of Music
807. *The Rocky Horror Show*
808. *Munchkinland* from The Wizard of Oz
809. *If I Were A Rich Man* – Fiddler On The Roof
810. *I'd Do Anything* – from Oliver

Gimme a Line

811. *Losing My Religion* – REM
812. *Wonderwall* – Oasis
813. *Every Breath You Take* – The Police
814. *Kiss* – Prince
815. *Tonight's The Night* – Rod Stewart
816. *Another One Bites The Dust* – Queen
817. *One Of These Nights* – The Eagles
818. *Flashdance (What A Feeling)* – Irene Cara
819. *It's Still Rock & Roll To Me* – Billy Joel
820. *Like A Virgin* – Madonna
821. *Song Sung Blue* – Neil Diamond
822. *My Sharona* – The Knack
823. *Bridge Over Troubled Water* – Simon and Garfunkel
824. *Ray Parker Jr* – Ghostbusters
825. *I Can't Stop Loving You* – Ray Charles
826. *Sailing* – Rod Stewart
827. *Always The Last To Know* – Del Amitri
828. *Maggie May* – Rod Stewart
829. *I Love Rock' N' Roll* – Joan Jett & The Heartbreaker
830. *Three Times A Lady* – The Commodores (Lionel Ritchie)
831. *We Are The Champions* – Queen
832. *Wake Me Up Before You Go-Go* – Wham
833. *Nothing Compares 2U* – Sinead O'Connor
834. *Faith* – George Michael
835. *Baby One More Time* – Britney Spears
836. *Dirrty* – Christina Aguilera
837. *Millennium* – Robbie Williams
838. *Angels* – Robbie Williams
839. *I'm A Believer* – The Monkees
840. *Should I Stay Or Should I Go* – The Clash
841. *Heroes* – David Bowie
842. *I Think I Love You* – The Partridge Family
843. *The Power of Love* – Huey Lewis and The News
844. *Walk On The Wildside* – Lou Reed
845. *Elevation* – U2
846. *Kiss* – Tom Jones
847. *Bette Davis Eyes* – Kim Carnes
848. *Black or White* – Michael Jackson

849. *Bat Out Of Hell* – Meat Loaf
850. *Like Prayer* – Madonna
851. *The Times They Are A Changin'* – Bob Dylan
852. *The Reflex* – Durtan Duran
853. *Don't You (Forget About Me)* – Simple Minds
854. *It Wasn't Me* – Shaggy
855. *You're So Vain* – Carly Simon
856. *We Don't Talk Anymore* – Cliff Richard
857. *China In Your Hand* – T'Pau
858. *Cracklin' Rosie* – Neil Diamond
859. *Goodbye Yellow Brick Road* – Elton John
860. *Do Ya Think I'm Sexy* – Rod Stewart
861. *Heart of Glass* – Blondie
862. *I Should Be So Lucky* – Kylie Minogue
863. *Dancing In The Dark* – Bruce Springsteen
864. *Lola* – The Kinks
865. *Superstition* – Stevie Wonder
866. *Y.M.C.A.* – Village People
867. *Walking in Memphis* – Marc Cohen
868. *All By Myself* – Eric Carmen
869. *Tragedy* – The Bee Gees
870. *Jump* – Van Halen
871. *Fairytale of New York* – The Pogues & Kirsty McCall
872. *Private Dancer* – Tina Turner
873. *The Boys Are Back In Town* – Thin Lizzy
874. *Alone Again (Naturally)* – Gilbert O'Sullivan
875. *Whiter Shade Of Pale* – Procul Harum
876. *Romeo and Juliet* – Dire Straits
877. *Come Fly With Me* – Frank Sinatra
878. *Smooth Criminal* – Michael Jackson
879. *She* – Charles Aznavour
880. *Last Train To London* – ELO
881. *Nights In White Satin* – The Moody Blues
882. *House of The Rising Sun* – The Animals
883. *Venus* – Bananarama (others)
884. *Simple Simon Says* – 1910 Fruitgum Company
885. *Sugar Sugar* – The Archies
886. *You Ain't Seen Nothing Yet* – Bachman Turner Overdrive
887. *Safety Dance* – Men Without Hats

888. *Drive* – The Cars
889. *Do They Know It's Christmas* – Band Aid
890. *You Sexy Thing* – Hot Chocolate
891. *I Walk The Line* – Johnny Cash
892. *Last Christmas* – Wham!
893. *Two Out Of Three Ain't Bad* – Meat Loaf
894. *Sweet Caroline* – Neil Diamond
895. *We've Got Tonight* – Kenny Rogers
896. *I Heard It Through The Grapevine* – Marvin Gaye (& others)
897. *Tracks of My Tears* – Smokey Robinson (& others)
898. *Thorn In My Side* – The Eurythmics
899. *Message In A Bottle* – The Police
900. *Radio Ga Ga* – Queen
901. *Whole Of The Moon* – The Waterboys
902. *Pretty Woman* – Roy Orbison
903. *The Winner Takes It All* – ABBA
904. *Mrs Robinson* – Simon & Garfunkel
905. *Rivers of Babylon* – Boney M
906. *Your Song* – Elton John
907. *Chain Reaction* – Diana Ross
908. *Get It On* – T-Rex
909. *Living On A Prayer* – Bon Jovi
910. *If You Leave Me Now* – Chicago
911. *Wonderful Tonight* – Eric Clapton
912. *Don't Stop* – Fleetwood Mac
913. *The Logical Song* – Supertramp
914. *Summer of' 69* – Bryan Adams
915. *Crazy Right Now* – Beyonce (Knowles)
916. *What's Your Flava?* – Craig David
917. *Going Underground* – The Jam
918. *I'll Be There For You* (Theme from Friends) – The Rembrants
919. *Together In Electric Dreams* – (Giorgio Moroder / Phil Oakey) – The Human League
920. *Hit Me With Your Rhythm Stick* – Ian Dury and The Blockheads
921. *No Woman No Cry* – Bob Marley
922. *Two Tribes* – Frankie Goes to Hollywood
923. *Close To You* – The Carpenters

924. *Baker Street* – Gerry Rafferty
925. *One Night In Bangkok* – Murray Head (from the musical Chess)
926. *You've Got A Friend* – James Taylor
927. *Billie Jean* – Michael Jackson
928. *Oliver's Army* – Elvis Costello / OK Go
929. *Baggy Trousers* – Madness
930. *I Can't Stop Loving You* – Ray Charles
931. *Wake Up Little Susie* – The Everly Brothers
932. *Let's Dance* – David Bowie
933. *Virginia Plain* – Roxy Music
934. *Woman* – John Lennon
935. *Band On The Run* – Paul McCartney and Wings
936. *Daydream Believer* – The Monkees
937. *Blueberry Hill* – Fats Domino
938. *Jealous Guy* – John Lennon / Bryan Ferry
939. *Hold Me Close* – David Essex
940. *I'm Not In Love* – 10CC
941. *Baby I Love You* – The Ramones
942. *Runaway* – Del Shannon
943. *The Sun Ain't Gonna Shine Anymore* – The Walker Brothers
944. *Angels* – Robbie Williams
945. *Material Girl* – Madonna
946. *Everything I Do I Do for You* – Bryan Adams
947. *All I Want Is You* – U2
948. *Time* – Pink Floyd (From Dark Side of the Moon)
949. *Keep On Loving You* – Reo Speedwagon
950. *Ballroom Blitz* – Sweet
951. *The Night Chicago Died* – Paper Lace
952. *Love Grows* – Edison Lighthouse
953. *Three Steps To Heaven* – Eddie Cochrane (Others)
954. *Love Is A Battlefield* – Pat Benatar
955. *Knocking On Heavens Door* – Bob Dylan / Guns 'n' Roses
956. *I Will Survive* – Gloria Gaynor
957. *Woman In Love* – Barbara Streisand
958. *In The Air Tonight* – Phil Collins
959. *Ruby Tuesday* – The Rolling Stones
960. *Hot Stuff* – Donna Summer

961. *King Of The Road* – Roger Miller (Others)
962. *Mr. Tambourine Man* – Bob Dylan / The Byrds
963. *Seasons In The Sun* – Terry Jacks / Westlife
964. *Something's Gotten Hold Of My Heart* – Gene Pitney / Marc Almond (Others)
965. *Make Me Smile (Come Up And See Me)* – Steve Harley & Cockney Rebel
966. *Don't Let The Sun Go Down On Me* – Elton John & George Michael
967. *The Joker* – Steve Miller
968. *Addicted To Love* – Robert Plamer
969. *Sunday Mornin' Comin' Down* – Kris Kristofferson
970. *The Mighty Quinn* – Bob Dylan / The Hollies
971. *Baby, Stop Crying* – Bob Dylan
972. *Pumping On Your Stereo* – Supergrass
973. *Walk This Way* – Aerosmith
974. *Bright Eyes* – Art Garfunkel
975. *Love Is All Around* – Wet Wet Wet
976. *Billy Don't Be A Hero* – Paper Lace
977. *The Tide Is High* – Blondie
978. *Can't Get You Out Of My Head* – Kylie Minogue
979. *Hungry Heart* – Bruce Springsteen
980. *Mama We're All Crazee Now* – Slade
981. *In The Navy* – Village People
982. *Believe* – Cher
983. *Gimme All Your Lovin'* – ZZ Top
984. *It Takes Two* – Tina Turner & Rod Stewart
985. *Money For Nothing* – Dire Straits
986. *Vincent* – Don McLean
987. *My Way* – Frank Sinatra
988. *We've Got Tonight* – Kenny Rogers
989. *Don't Stand So Close To Me* – The Police
990. *It's a Kind Of Magic* – Queen
991. *Knowing Me Knowing You* – ABBA
992. *Vogue* – Madonna
993. *Cecelia* – Simon & Garfunkel
994. *Brown Girl In The Ring* – Boney M
995. *Upside Down* – Diana Ross
996. *Layla* – Derek & The Dominoes
997. *Town Called Malice* – The Jam

998. *Unchained Melody* – The Righteous Brothers /
Gareth Gates
999. *Eye of The Tiger* – Survivor
1000. *Wannabe* – The Spice Girls
1001. *I'm A Believer* – The Monkees

The Bonus Tracks

The Sixties

1002. The Kinks – *Sunny Afternoon*
1003. Small Faces – *Lazy Sunday Afternoon*
1004. Mamas And The Papas – *California Dreamin'*
1005. Thunderclap Newman – *Something In The Air*
1006. Dusty Springfield – *Son of a Preacher Man*
1007. Gary Puckett And The Union Gap – *Young Girl*
1008. Simon & Garfunkel – *Mrs. Robinson*
1009. The Hollies – *The Air That I Breathe*
1010. Herman's Hermits – *I'm Into Something Good*
1011. Donovan – *Jennifer Juniper*
1012. New Vaudeville Band – *Winchester Cathedral*
1013. The Monkees – *Daydream Believer*
1014. Engelbert Humperdinck – *There Goes My Everything*
1015. The Move – *Flowers in the Rain*
1016. Keith West – *Excerpt From A Teenage Opera*
1017. The Kinks (Dave Davies) – *Death of a Clown*
1018. Cat Stevens – *Matthew and Son*
1019. The Kinks – *Dedicated Follower of Fashion*
1020. The Troggs – *With A Girl Like You*
1021. The Troggs – *Love Is All Around*
1022. The Beatles – *Yellow Submarine*
1023. Manfred Mann – *Pretty Flamingo*
1024. Gerry and The Pacemakers – *You'll Never Walk Alone*
1025. John Fred & His Playboy Band – *Judy in Disguise
(with glasses)*

The Seventies

1026. Edison Lighthouse – *Love Grows Where My
Rosemary Goes*
1027. Mungo Jerry – *In The Summertime*

1028. The New Seekers – *I'd Like To Teach The World To Sing*
1029. Neil Diamond – *I Am I Said*
1030. Rod Stewart – *You Wear It Well*
1031. The Ch-Lites – *Have You Seen Her*
1032. The Faces – *Stay With Me*
1033. 10CC – *Rubber Bullets*
1034. Peters & Lee – *Welcome Home*
1035. David Cassidy – *Daydreamer*
1036. Mud – *Tiger Feet*
1037. ABBA – *Waterloo*
1038. Steve Harley & Cockney Rebel – *Come Up And See Me (Make Me Smile)*
1039. David Bowie – *Life On Mars*
1040. Elkie Brooks – *Pearl's A Singer*
1041. Leo Sayer – *When I Need You*
1042. C.W. McCall – *Convoy*
1043. Tavares – *Don't Take Away The Music*
1044. The Bee Gees – *Night Fever*
1045. Blondie – *Sunday Girl*
1046. Cliff Richard – *We Don't Talk Anymore*
1047. The Police – *Message In A Bottle*
1048. Elton John – *Your Song*
1049. Pilot – *January*

The Eighties

1050. Nena – *99 Red Balloons*
1051. The Jam – *Going Underground*
1052. David Bowie – *Ashes To Ashes*
1053. John Lennon – *Imagine*
1054. The Nolans – *I'm In The Mood For Dancin'*
1055. Bucks Fizz – *Making Your Mind Up*
1056. Europe – *The Final Countdown*
1057. Phil Collins – *You Can't Hurry Love*
1058. Bonnie Tyler – *Total Eclipse of the Heart*
1059. Paul Young – *Wherever I Lay My Hat*
1060. Billy Joel – *Uptown Girl*
1061. George Michael – *Careless Whisper*
1062. Sister Sledge – *Lost in Music*
1063. Kelly Marie – *Feels Like I'm In Love*

Name that Song!

1064. Cliff Richard (The Young Ones) – *Living Doll*
1065. The Communards – *Don't Leave Me This Way*
1066. The Bee Gees – *You Win Again*
1067. Aretha Franklin & George Michael – *I Knew You Were Waiting*
1068. Marc Almond (Gene Pitney) – *Something's Gotten Hold Of My Heart*
1069. Whitney Houston – *One Moment In Time*
1070. Jason Donovan – *Too Many Broken Hearts*
1071. Madonna – *Express Yourself*
1072. Elvis Costello – *Good Year For The Roses*
1073. Madness – *Baggy Trousers*

The Nineties
1074. Maria McKee – *Show Me Heaven*
1075. Beautiful South – *A Little Time*
1076. Iron Maiden – *Bring Your Daughter To The Slaughter*
1077. Jason Donovan – *Any Dream Will Do*
1078. Michael Jackson – *Black Or White*
1079. Shaggy – *Oh Carolina*
1080. Madonna – *Vogue*
1081. Simpsons – *Do The Bartman*
1082. Freddie Mercury – *Living On My Own*
1083. D:Ream – *Things Can Only Get Better*
1084. Mariah Carey (Harry Nilsson) – *Without You*
1085. Whigfield – *Saturday Night*
1086. East 17 – *Stay Another Day*
1087. Take That – *Back For Good*
1088. Oasis – *Don't Look Back In Anger*
1089. The Spice Girls – *Wannabe*
1090. Deep Blue Something – *Breakfast At Tiffany's*
1091. Cornershop – *Brimful of Asha*
1092. Westlife – *Flying Without Wings*
1093. Boyzone – *Words (Bee Gees)*
1094. Aqua – *Barbie Girl*
1095. B*witched – *C'est La Vie*
1096. Lou Bega – *Mambo #5*
1097. Robbie Williams – *She's The One*

1098. Britney Spears – *Oops!...I Did It Again*

1099.   Eminem – *The Real Slim Shady*
1100.   U2 – *Beautiful Day*
1101.   Atomic Kitten – *Whole Again*
1102.   Shaggy – *It Wasn't Me*
1103.   S Club 7 – *Don't Stop Movin'*
1104.   Bob The Builder – *Can We Fix It?*
1105.   Westlife – *Queen Of My Heart*
1106.   Pink – *Just Like A Pill*
1107.   Tatu – *All The Things She Said*
1108.   Girls Aloud – *Sound Of The Underground*
1109.   Peter Andre – *Mysterious Girl*
1110.   All Star – *Shrek*

Create Your Own Pop-Pickers Quiz

Who had a hit with....?
Name the song that....?
What year was.....?

To get started and make it easier why not use the following.

Reference listing of selected Chart Hits (UK) 1960 – 2004

Jan-60	Michael Holliday	Starry Eyed
Jan-60	Anthony Newley	Why
Jan-60	Adam Faith	Poor Me
Feb-60	Johnny Preston	Running Bear
Mar-60	Anthony Newley	Do You Mind
Mar-60	Lonnie Donegan & His Group	My Old Man's A Dustman (Ballad Of A Refuse Disposal Officer)
Apr-60	Everly Brothers	Cathy's Clown
May-60	Eddie Cochran	Three Steps To Heaven
Jun-60	Jimmy Jones	Good Timin'
Jun-60	Johnny Kidd & The Pirates	Shakin' All Over
Jun-60	Cliff Richard & The Shadows	Please Don't Tease
Jul-60	The Shadows	Apache
Aug-60	Roy Orbison	Only The Lonely
Aug-60	Ricky Valance	Tell Laura I Love Her
Nov-60	Elvis Presley with The Jordanaires	It's Now Or Never
Dec-60	Cliff Richard & The Shadows	I Love You
Dec-60	Johnny Tillotson	Poetry In Motion
Jan-61	Elvis Presley with The Jordanaires	Are You Lonesome Tonight?

Name that Song!

Jan-61	Petula Clark	Sailor
Feb-61	Everly Brothers	Walk Right Back / Ebony Eyes
Mar-61	Elvis Presley	Wooden Heart
Mar-61	Temperance Seven	You're Driving Me Crazy
Apr-61	Marcels	Blue Moon
Apr-61	Floyd Cramer	On The Rebound
Apr-61	Del Shannon	Runaway
May-61	Elvis Presley with The Jordanaires	Surrender (Torna Surriento)
Jun-61	Eden Kane	Well I Ask You
Jun-61	Everly Brothers	Temptation
Jun-61	Helen Shapiro	You Don't Know
Jul-61	Shirley Bassey	Reach For The Stars / Climb Ev'ry Mountain
Aug-61	John Leyton	Johnny Remember Me
Sep-61	Shadows	Kon-Tiki
Sep-61	Highwaymen	Michael
Sep-61	Helen Shapiro	Walkin' Back To Happiness
Nov-61	Elvis Presley	(Marie's The Name) His Latest Flame / Little Sister
Nov-61	Danny Williams	Moon River
Nov-61	Frankie Vaughan	Tower Of Strength
Jan-62	Cliff Richard & The Shadows	The Young Ones
Feb-62	Elvis Presley with The Jordanaires	Rock A Hula Baby / Can't Help Falling In Love
Mar-62	Shadows	Wonderful Land
Apr-62	B Bumble & The Stingers	Nut Rocker
May-62	Mike Sarne with Wendy Richard	Come Outside
May-62	Elvis Presley with The Jordanaires	Good Luck Charm
Jun-62	Ray Charles	I Can't Stop Loving You
Jul-62	Frank Ifield	I Remember You
Aug-62	Elvis Presley with The Jordanaires	She's Not You
Aug-62	Tornados	Telstar

Oct-62	Frank Ifield	Lovesick Blues
Nov-62	Elvis Presley with The Jordanaires	Return To Sender
Dec-62	Cliff Richard, The Shadows & The Norrie Paramor Strings	The Next Time / Bachelor Boy
Jan-64	Bachelors	Diane
Jan-64	Searchers	Needles And Pins
Feb-64	Cilla Black	Anyone Who Had A Heart
Feb-64	Billy J Kramer & The Dakotas	Little Children
Mar-64	Peter & Gordon	A World Without Love
Mar-64	Beatles	Can't Buy Me Love
Apr-64	Four Pennies	Juliet / Tell Me Girl (What Are You Gonna Do)
Apr-64	Searchers	Don't Throw Your Love Away
Apr-64	Roy Orbison	It's Over
May-64	Cilla Black	You're My World
Jun-64	Animals	House Of The Rising Sun
Jul-64	Rolling Stones	It's All Over Now
Jul-64	Beatles	A Hard Day's Night
Jul-64	Manfred Mann	Do Wah Diddy Diddy
Jul-64	Honeycombs	Have I The Right
Aug-64	Kinks	You Really Got Me
Aug-64	Herman's Hermits	I'm Into Something Good
Sep-64	Roy Orbison	Oh Pretty Woman
Oct-64	Sandie Shaw	(There's) Always Something There To Remind Me
Oct-64	Supremes	Baby Love
Nov-64	Rolling Stones	Little Red Rooster
Dec-64	Beatles	I Feel Fine
Dec-64	Moody Blues	Go Now
Dec-64	Georgie Fame & The Blue Flames	Yeh Yeh
Jan-65	Seekers	I'll Never Find Another You
Jan-65	Righteous Brothers	You've Lost That Lovin' Feelin'

Name that Song!

Jan-65	Kinks	Tired Of Waiting For You
Feb-65	Tom Jones	It's Not Unusual
Feb-65	Unit Four Plus Two	Concrete And Clay
Mar-65	Rolling Stones	The Last Time
Mar-65	Cliff Richard	The Minute You're Gone
Mar-65	Roger Miller	King Of The Road
Apr-65	Beatles	Ticket To Ride
Apr-65	Jackie Trent	Where Are You Now (My Love)
May-65	Sandie Shaw	Long Live Love
May-65	Elvis Presley with The Jordanaires	Crying In The Chapel
May-65	Hollies	I'm Alive
Jun-65	Byrds	Mr Tambourine Man
Jul-65	Beatles	Help!
Aug-65	Sonny & Cher	I Got You Babe
Aug-65	Walker Brothers	Make It Easy On Yourself
Aug-65	Rolling Stones	(I Can't Get No) Satisfaction
Sep-65	Ken Dodd	Tears
Oct-65	Rolling Stones	Get Off My Cloud
Oct-65	Seekers	The Carnival Is Over
Dec-65	Spencer Davis Group	Keep On Running
Dec-65	Beatles	Day Tripper / We Can Work It Out
Jan-66	Overlanders	Michelle
Jan-66	Nancy Sinatra	These Boots Are Made For Walking
Mar-66	Walker Brothers	The Sun Ain't Gonna Shine Anymore
Mar-66	Spencer Davis Group	Somebody Help Me
Mar-66	Dusty Springfield	You Don't Have To Say You Love Me
Apr-66	Manfred Mann	Pretty Flamingo
May-66	Frank Sinatra	Strangers In The Night
May-66	Rolling Stones	Paint It Black
Jun-66	Kinks	Sunny Afternoon
Jun-66	Beatles	Paperback Writer
Jun-66	Georgie Fame & The Blue Flames	Get Away

Jun-66	Chris Farlowe	Out Of Time
Jul-66	Troggs	With A Girl Like You
Aug-66	Small Faces	All Or Nothing
Aug-66	Beatles	Yellow Submarine / Eleanor Rigby
Aug-66	Jim Reeves	Distant Drums
Oct-66	Four Tops	Reach Out I'll Be There
Nov-66	Beach Boys	Good Vibrations
Nov-66	Tom Jones	Green Green Grass Of Home
Jan-67	Monkees	I'm A Believer
Jan-67	Engelbert Humperdinck	Release Me
Feb-67	Petula Clark	This Is My Song
Mar-67	Sandie Shaw	Puppet On A String
Mar-67	Nancy Sinatra & Frank Sinatra	Somethin' Stupid
Apr-67	Tremeloes	Silence Is Golden
May-67	Procol Harum	A Whiter Shade Of Pale
Jul-67	Beatles	All You Need Is Love
Jul-67	Scott McKenzie	San Francisco (Wear Some Flowers In Your Hair)
Aug-67	Engelbert Humperdinck	The Last Waltz
Sep-67	Bee Gees	Massachusetts
Sep-67	Foundations	Baby Now That I've Found You
Nov-67	Long John Baldry	Let The Heartaches Begin
Nov-67	Beatles	Hello Goodbye
Dec-67	Georgie Fame	Ballad Of Bonnie And Clyde
Jan-68	Love Affair	Everlasting Love
Jan-68	Manfred Mann	Mighty Quinn
Feb-68	Louis Armstrong	What A Wonderful World
Feb-68	Esther & Abi Ofarim	Cinderella Rockefella
Feb-68	Dave Dee Dozy Beaky Mick & Tich	Legend Of Xanadu
Mar-68	Cliff Richard	Congratulations
Mar-68	Beatles	Lady Madonna
Apr-68	Tommy James & The Shondells	Mony Mony
Apr-68	Union Gap featuring	

	Gary Puckett	Young Girl
May-68	Des O'Connor	I Pretend
May-68	Equals	Baby Come Back
May-68	Rolling Stones	Jumping Jack Flash
Jun-68	Crazy World Of Arthur Brown	Fire
Jul-68	Beach Boys	Do It Again
Aug-68	Bee Gees	I've Gotta Get A Message To You
Sep-68	Beatles	Hey Jude
Sep-68	Mary Hopkin	Those Were The Days
Sep-68	Hugo Montenegro	The Good The Bad And The Ugly
Oct-68	Joe Cocker	With A Little Help From My Friends
Nov-68	Scaffold	Lily The Pink
Dec-68	Fleetwood Mac	Albatross
Dec-68	Marmalade	Ob-La-Di Ob-La-Da
Dec-68	Move	Blackberry Way
Jan-69	Amen Corner	(If Paradise Is) Half As Nice
Feb-69	Peter Sarstedt	Where Do You Go To My Lovely
Feb-69	Marvin Gaye	I Heard It Through The Grapevine
Mar-69	Desmond Dekker & Aces	Israelites
Apr-69	Tommy Roe	Dizzy
Apr-69	Beatles with Billy Preston	Get Back
Jun-69	Beatles	Ballad Of John And Yoko
Jun-69	Thunderclap Newman	Something In The Air
Jul-69	Rolling Stones	Honky Tonk Women
Aug-69	Zager & Evans	In The Year 2525
Aug-69	Creedence Clearwater Revival	Bad Moon Rising
Aug-69	Bobbie Gentry	I'll Never Fall In Love Again
Oct-69	Jane Birkin & Serge Gainsbourg	Je T'Aime... Moi Non Plus
Oct-69	Archies	Sugar Sugar

Nov-69	Rolf Harris	Two Little Boys
Jan-70	Edison Lighthouse	Love Grows (Where My Rosemary Goes)
Feb-70	Lee Marvin	Wand'rin' Star
Feb-70	Simon & Garfunkel	Bridge Over Troubled Water
Mar-70	Norman Greenbaum	Spirit In The Sky
Apr-70	Dana	All Kinds Of Everything
Apr-70	England World Cup Squad	Back Home
May-70	Christie	Yellow River
Jun-70	Mungo Jerry	In The Summertime
Jul-70	Elvis Presley	The Wonder Of You
Aug-70	Smokey Robinson & The Miracles	The Tears Of A Clown
Sep-70	Freda Payne	Band Of Gold
Sep-70	Matthews Southern Comfort	Woodstock
Nov-70	Jimi Hendrix Experience	Voodoo Chile
Nov-70	Dave Edmunds	I Hear You Knocking
Nov-70	Clive Dunn	Grandad
Jan-71	George Harrison	My Sweet Lord
Feb-71	Mungo Jerry	Baby Jump
Feb-71	T Rex	Hot Love
Mar-71	Dave & Ansil Collins	Double Barrel
Apr-71	Dawn	Knock Three Times
Jun-71	Middle Of The Road	Chirpy Chirpy Cheep Cheep
Jul-71	T Rex	Get It On
Jul-71	Tams	Hey Girl Don't Bother Me
Jul-71	Diana Ross	I'm Still Waiting
Sep-71	Rod Stewart	Maggie May
Oct-71	Slade	Coz I Luv You
Nov-71	Benny Hill	Ernie (The Fastest Milkman In The West)
Dec-71	New Seekers	I'd Like To Teach The World To Sing
Jan-72	Chicory Tip	Son Of My Father
Jan-72	T Rex	Telegram Sam
Feb-72	Nilsson	Without You

Apr-72	The Royal Scots Dragoon Guards	Amazing Grace
May-72	T Rex	Metal Guru
May-72	Don McLean	Vincent
Jun-72	Slade	Take Me Bak 'Ome
Jun-72	Donny Osmond	Puppy Love
Jul-72	Alice Cooper	School's Out
Aug-72	Rod Stewart	You Wear It Well
Sep-72	Slade	Mama Weer All Crazee Now
Sep-72	David Cassidy	How Can I Be Sure
Sep-72	Lieutenant Pigeon	Mouldy Old Dough
Oct-72	Gilbert O'Sullivan	Clair
Oct-72	Chuck Berry	My Ding-A-Ling
Nov-72	Little Jimmy Osmond	Long Haired Lover From Liverpool
Jan-73	Sweet	Blockbuster
Mar-73	Slade	Cum On Feel The Noize
Mar-73	Donny Osmond	The Twelfth Of Never
Mar-73	Dawn featuring Tony Orlando	Tie A Yellow Ribbon Round The Old Oak Tree
Mar-73	Gilbert O'Sullivan	Get Down
Apr-73	Wizzard	See My Baby Jive
May-73	Suzi Quatro	Can The Can
May-73	10CC	Rubber Bullets
May-73	Peters & Lee	Welcome Home
Jun-73	Slade	Skweeze Me Pleeze Me
Jul-73	Gary Glitter	I'm The Leader Of The Gang (I Am)
Aug-73	Donny Osmond	Young Love
Sep-73	Wizzard	Angel Fingers
Sep-73	Simon Park Orchestra	Eye Level
Oct-73	David Cassidy	Daydreamer / The Puppy Song
Nov-73	Gary Glitter	I Love You Love Me Love
Nov-73	New Seekers	You Won't Find Another Fool Like Me
Dec-73	Slade	Merry Xmas Everybody
Jan-74	Mud	Tiger Feet
Feb-74	Suzi Quatro	Devil Gate Drive

Feb-74	Alvin Stardust	Jealous Mind
Feb-74	Paper Lace	Billy Don't Be A Hero
Mar-74	Terry Jacks	Seasons In The Sun
Apr-74	Abba	Waterloo
May-74	Rubettes	Sugar Baby Love
May-74	Ray Stevens	The Streak
Jun-74	Gary Glitter	Always Yours
Jun-74	Charles Aznavour	She
Jun-74	George McCrae	Rock Your Baby
Jul-74	Three Degrees	When Will I See You Again
Aug-74	John Denver	Annie's Song
Aug-74	Carl Douglas	Kung Fu Fighting
Aug-74	Osmonds	Love Me For A Reason
Sep-74	Sweet Sensation	Sad Sweet Dreamer
Sep-74	Ken Boothe	Everything I Own
Oct-74	David Essex	Gonna Make You A Star
Nov-74	Barry White	You're The First The Last My Everything
Nov-74	Mud	Lonely This Christmas
Dec-74	Status Quo	Down Down
Dec-74	Tymes	Ms Grace
Jan-75	Pilot	January
Feb-75	Steve Harley & Cockney Rebel	Make Me Smile (Come Up And See Me)
Feb-75	Telly Savalas	If
Mar-75	Bay City Rollers	Bye Bye Baby
Apr-75	Mud	Oh Boy
Apr-75	Tammy Wynette	Stand By Your Man
May-75	Windsor Davies & Don Estelle	Whispering Grass
May-75	10CC	I'm Not In Love
Jun-75	Johnny Nash	Tears On My Pillow
Jul-75	Typically Tropical	Barbados
Jul-75	Bay City Rollers	Give A Little Love
Jul-75	Stylistics	Can't Give You Anything (But My Love)
Aug-75	Rod Stewart	Sailing
Sep-75	David Essex	Hold Me Close
Sep-75	Art Garfunkel	I Only Have Eyes For You
Oct-75	David Bowie	Space Oddity

Name that Song!

Nov-75	Billy Connolly	D.I.V.O.R.C.E.
Nov-75	Queen	Bohemian Rhapsody
Dec-75	Abba	Mamma Mia
Jan-76	Slik	Forever And Ever
Jan-76	Four Seasons	December 1963 (Oh What A Night)
Feb-76	Tina Charles	I Love To Love
Mar-76	Brotherhood Of Man	Save Your Kisses For Me
Mar-76	Abba	Fernando
Apr-76	J J Barrie	No Charge
May-76	Wurzels	Combine Harvester (Brand New Key)
Jun-76	Real Thing	You To Me Are Everything
Jun-76	Demis Roussos	The Roussos Phenomenon EP
Jul-76	Elton John & Kiki Dee	Don't Go Breaking My Heart
Aug-76	Abba	Dancing Queen
Aug-76	Pussycat	Mississippi
Oct-76	Chicago	If You Leave Me Now
Nov-76	Showaddywaddy	Under The Moon Of Love
Nov-76	Johnny Mathis	When A Child Is Born
Dec-76	David Soul	Don't Give Up On Us
Dec-76	Julie Covington	Don't Cry For Me Argentina
Jan-77	Leo Sayer	When I Need You
Feb-77	Manhattan Transfer	Chanson D'Amour
Feb-77	Abba	Knowing Me Knowing You
Apr-77	Deniece Williams	Free
Apr-77	Rod Stewart	I Don't Want To Talk About It / First Cut Is The Deepest
Apr-77	Kenny Rogers	Lucille
Jun-77	Jacksons	Show You The Way To Go
Jun-77	Hot Chocolate	So You Win Again
Jul-77	Brotherhood Of Man	Angelo
Jul-77	Donna Summer	I Feel Love
Jul-77	Floaters	Float On
Aug-77	Elvis Presley	Way Down
Aug-77	David Soul	Silver Lady

Sep-77	Baccara	Yes Sir I Can Boogie
Oct-77	Abba	The Name Of The Game
Nov-77	Wings	Mull Of Kintyre / Girls' School
Dec-77	Althia & Donna	Up Town Top Ranking
Jan-78	Brotherhood Of Man	Figaro
Feb-78	Abba	Take A Chance On Me
Feb-78	Kate Bush	Wuthering Heights
Feb-78	Brian & Michael	Matchstalk Men And Matchstalk Cats And Dogs
Apr-78	Bee Gees	Night Fever
Apr-78	Boney M	Rivers Of Babylon / Brown Girl In The Ring
May-78	John Travolta & Olivia Newton-John	You're The One That I Want
Aug-78	Commodores	Three Times A Lady
Aug-78	10CC	Dreadlock Holiday
Sep-78	John Travolta & Olivia Newton-John	Summer Nights
Oct-78	Boomtown Rats	Rat Trap
Nov-78	Rod Stewart	Da Ya Think I'm Sexy?
Nov-78	Village People	Y.M.C.A.
Dec-78	Boney M	Mary's Boy Child – Oh My Lord
Dec-78	Ian Dury & Blockheads	Hit Me With Your Rhythm Stick
Jan-79	Blondie	Heart Of Glass
Feb-79	Gloria Gaynor	I Will Survive
Feb-79	Bee Gees	Tragedy
Mar-79	Art Garfunkel	Bright Eyes
May-79	Tubeway Army	Are Friends Electric
May-79	Blondie	Sunday Girl
Jun-79	Anita Ward	Ring My Bell
Jul-79	Boomtown Rats	I Don't Like Mondays
Jul-79	Cliff Richard	We Don't Talk Anymore
Sep-79	Gary Numan	Cars
Sep-79	Police	Message In A Bottle
Sep-79	Buggles	Video Killed The Radio Star
Sep-79	Dr Hook	When You're In Love

		With A Beautiful Woman
Sep-79	Lena Martell	One Day At A Time
Nov-79	Pretenders	Brass In Pocket
Dec-79	Pink Floyd	Another Brick In The Wall
Dec-79	Police	Walking On The Moon
Jan-80	Kenny Rogers	Coward Of The County
Jan-80	Special AKA	The Special AKA Live EP
Feb-80	Fern Kinney	Together We Are Beautiful
Feb-80	Blondie	Atomic
Feb-80	Detroit Spinners	Working My Way Back To You – Forgive Me Girl
Mar-80	Dexy's Midnight Runners	Geno
Mar-80	Jam	Going Underground / Dreams Of Children
Apr-80	Blondie	Call Me
May-80	Johnny Logan	What's Another Year
May-80	Don McLean	Crying
May-80	MASH	Theme From M.A.S.H. (Suicide Is Painless)
Jun-80	Odyssey	Use It Up And Wear It Out
Jun-80	Olivia Newton-John & ELO	Xanadu
Aug-80	Kelly Marie	Feels Like I'm In Love
Aug-80	Abba	The Winner Takes It All
Aug-80	David Bowie	Ashes To Ashes
Aug-80	Jam	Start
Sep-80	Police	Don't Stand So Close To Me
Oct-80	Barbra Streisand	Woman In Love
Nov-80	John Lennon	(Just Like) Starting Over
Nov-80	Blondie	The Tide Is High
Nov-80	Abba	Super Trouper
Nov-80	St Winifred's School Choir	There's No One Quite Like Grandma
Dec-80	John Lennon	Imagine
Jan-81	John Lennon	Woman
Feb-81	Joe Dolce Music Theatre	Shaddup You Face
Feb-81	Roxy Music	Jealous Guy
Feb-81	Shakin' Stevens	This Ole House

Mar-81	Bucks Fizz	Making Your Mind Up
May-81	Smokey Robinson	Being With You
May-81	Adam & The Ants	Stand And Deliver
May-81	Michael Jackson	One Day In Your Life
Jun-81	Specials	Ghost Town
Jul-81	Shakin' Stevens	Green Door
Aug-81	Soft Cell	Tainted Love
Aug-81	Aneka	Japanese Boy
Sep-81	Adam & The Ants	Prince Charming
Sep-81	Dave Stewart with Barbara Gaskin	It's My Party
Oct-81	Julio Iglesias	Begin The Beguine
Oct-81	Police	Every Little Thing She Does Is Magic
Nov-81	Queen & David Bowie	Under Pressure
Nov-81	Bucks Fizz	The Land Of Make Believe
Dec-81	Human League	Don't You Want Me
Dec-81	Kraftwerk	The Model / Computer Love
Jan-82	Shakin' Stevens	Oh Julie
Jan-82	Tight Fit	The Lion Sleeps Tonight
Feb-82	Jam	Town Called Malice / Precious
Feb-82	Goombay Dance Band	Seven Tears
Mar-82	Bucks Fizz	My Camera Never Lies
Apr-82	Paul McCartney with Stevie Wonder	Ebony And Ivory
May-82	Nicole	A Little Peace
May-82	Charlene	I've Never Been To Me
May-82	Adam Ant	Goody Two Shoes
May-82	Madness	House Of Fun
Jun-82	Captain Sensible	Happy Talk
Jul-82	Dexy's Midnight Runners	Come On Eileen
Jul-82	Irene Cara	Fame
Jul-82	Survivor	Eye Of The Tiger
Sep-82	Culture Club	Do You Really Want To Hurt Me
Sep-82	Musical Youth	Pass The Dutchie
Oct-82	Eddy Grant	I Don't Wanna Dance
Oct-82	Renee & Renato	Save Your Love

Name that Song!

Dec-82	Jam	Beat Surrender
Dec-82	Phil Collins	You Can't Hurry Love
Jan-83	Men At Work	Down Under
Jan-83	Kajagoogoo	Too Shy
Jan-83	Michael Jackson	Billie Jean
Feb-83	Bonnie Tyler	Total Eclipse Of The Heart
Mar-83	Duran Duran	Is There Something I Should Know
Mar-83	David Bowie	Let's Dance
Apr-83	New Edition	Candy Girl
Apr-83	Spandau Ballet	True
May-83	Police	Every Breath You Take
Jun-83	Rod Stewart	Baby Jane
Jun-83	Paul Young	Wherever I Lay My Hat (That's My Home)
Jul-83	KC & The Sunshine Band	Give It Up
Aug-83	UB40	Red Red Wine
Sep-83	Culture Club	Karma Chameleon
Oct-83	Billy Joel	Uptown Girl
Nov-83	Frankie Goes To Hollywood	Relax
Nov-83	Flying Pickets	Only You
Dec-83	Paul McCartney	Pipes Of Peace
Feb-84	Nena	99 Red Balloons
Mar-84	Lionel Richie	Hello
Apr-84	Duran Duran	The Reflex
May-84	Wham!	Wake Me Up Before You Go Go
Jun-84	Frankie Goes To Hollywood	Two Tribes
Aug-84	George Michael	Careless Whisper
Aug-84	Stevie Wonder	I Just Called To Say I Love You
Oct-84	Wham!	Freedom
Oct-84	Chaka Khan	I Feel For You
Nov-84	Jim Diamond	I Should Have Known Better
Dec-84	Frankie Goes To Hollywood	The Power Of Love
Dec-84	Foreigner	I Want To Know What

		Love Is
Dec-84	Band Aid	Do They Know It's Christmas
Jan-85	Elaine Paige & Barbara Dickson	I Know Him So Well
Feb-85	Phyllis Nelson	Move Closer
Mar-85	Philip Bailey duet with Phil Collins	Easy Lover
Mar-85	Dead Or Alive	You Spin Me Round (Like A Record)
Apr-85	USA For Africa	We Are The World
May-85	Paul Hardcastle	Nineteen
Jun-85	Sister Sledge	Frankie
Jun-85	Crowd	You'll Never Walk Alone
Jun-85	Jennifer Rush	The Power Of Love
Jul-85	Eurythmics	There Must Be An Angel (Playing With My Heart)
Jul-85	Madonna	Into The Groove
Aug-85	UB40 featuring Chrissie Hynde	I Got You Babe
Sep-85	David Bowie & Mick Jagger	Dancing In The Street
Sep-85	Midge Ure	If I Was
Oct-85	Feargal Sharkey	A Good Heart
Nov-85	Whitney Houston	Saving All My Love For You
Nov-85	Wham!	I'm Your Man
Nov-85	Pet Shop Boys	West End Girls
Dec-85	Shakin' Stevens	Merry Christmas Everyone
Dec-85	A-Ha	The Sun Always Shines On TV
Jan-86	Diana Ross	Chain Reaction
Jan-86	Billy Ocean	When The Going Gets Tough The Tough Get Going
Mar-86	Cliff Richard & The Young Ones featuring Hank Marvin	Living Doll
Mar-86	Falco	Rock Me Amadeus

Apr-86	George Michael	A Different Corner
May-86	Dr & The Medics	Spirit In The Sky
May-86	Spitting Image	The Chicken Song
Jun-86	Wham!	The Edge Of Heaven / Where Did Your Heart Go
Jun-86	Madonna	Papa Don't Preach
Jul-86	Chris De Burgh	The Lady In Red
Jul-86	Boris Gardiner	I Want To Wake Up With You
Aug-86	Communards	Don't Leave Me This Way
Oct-86	Nick Berry	Every Loser Wins
Oct-86	Madonna	True Blue
Oct-86	Berlin	Take My Breath Away
Nov-86	Europe	The Final Countdown
Nov-86	Jackie Wilson	Reet Petite (The Sweetest Girl In Town)
Dec-86	Housemartins	Caravan Of Love
Jan-87	Steve 'Silk' Hurley	Jack Your Body
Jan-87	Aretha Franklin & George Michael	I Knew You Were Waiting (For Me)
Feb-87	Ben E King	Stand By Me
Mar-87	Boy George	Everything I Own
Mar-87	Mel & Kim	Respectable
Apr-87	Madonna	La Isla Bonita
Apr-87	Ferry Aid	Let It Be
Apr-87	Starship	Nothing's Gonna Stop Us Now
May-87	Whitney Houston	I Wanna Dance With Somebody (Who Loves Me)
Jun-87	Firm	Star Trekkin'
Jun-87	Pet Shop Boys	It's A Sin
Jul-87	Los Lobos	La Bamba
Jul-87	Madonna	Who's That Girl
Aug-87	Michael Jackson	I Just Can't Stop Loving You
Aug-87	Rick Astley	Never Gonna Give You Up
Sep-87	Marrs	Pump Up The Volume
Sep-87	Bee Gees	You Win Again
Oct-87	T'Pau	China In Your Hand

Create Your Own Pop-Pickers Quiz

Dec-87	Pet Shop Boys	Always On My Mind
Dec-87	Belinda Carlisle	Heaven Is A Place On Earth
Jan-88	Tiffany	I Think We're Alone Now
Jan-88	Kylie Minogue	I Should Be So Lucky
Feb-88	Aswad	Don't Turn Around
Apr-88	Pet Shop Boys	Heart
Apr-88	Fairground Attraction	Perfect
Apr-88	S Express	Theme From S'Express
May-88	Billy Bragg with Cara Tivey	She's Leaving Home
May-88	Wet Wet Wet	With A Little Help From My Friends
Jun-88	Timelords	Doctorin' The Tardis
Jun-88	Bros	I Owe You Nothing
Jun-88	Glenn Medeiros	Nothing's Gonna Change My Love For You
Jul-88	Yazz & The Plastic Population	The Only Way Is Up
Sep-88	Phil Collins	A Groovy Kind Of Love
Sep-88	Hollies	He Ain't Heavy He's My Brother
Sep-88	Whitney Houston	One Moment In Time
Oct-88	U2	Desire
Oct-88	Enya	Orinoco Flow
Oct-88	Robin Beck	First Time
Dec-88	Cliff Richard	Mistletoe And Wine
Dec-88	Kylie Minogue & Jason Donovan	Especially For You
Jan-89	Marc Almond featuring Gene Pitney	Something's Gotten Hold Of My Heart
Feb-89	Simple Minds	Belfast Child
Feb-89	Bangles	Eternal Flame
Mar-89	Jason Donovan	Too Many Broken Hearts
Mar-89	Madonna	Like A Prayer
May-89	Kylie Minogue	Hand On Your Heart
May-89	Christians, Holly Johnson, Paul McCartney, Gerry Marsden & Stock	

	Aitken Waterman	Ferry 'Cross The Mersey
Jun-89	Soul II Soul featuring Caron Wheeler	Back To Life (However Do You Want Me)
Jun-89	Jason Donovan	Sealed With A Kiss
Jun-89	Sonia	You'll Never Stop Me From Loving You
Jul-89	Jive Bunny & The Mastermixers	Swing The Mood
Aug-89	Black Box	Ride On Time
Oct-89	Jive Bunny & The Mastermixers	That's What I Like
Oct-89	Lisa Stansfield	All Around The World
Nov-89	New Kids On The Block	You Got It (The Right Stuff)
Dec-89	Jive Bunny & The Mastermixers	Let's Party
Dec-89	Band Aid II	Do They Know It's Christmas
Jan-90	New Kids On The Block	Hangin' Tough
Jan-90	Sinead O'Connor	Nothing Compares 2 U
Jan-90	Kylie Minogue	Tears On My Pillow
Feb-90	Beats International featuring Lindy Layton	Dub Be Good To Me
Mar-90	Snap	The Power
Apr-90	Adamski	Killer
Apr-90	Madonna	Vogue
Jun-90	Englandneworder	World In Motion
Jun-90	Elton John	Sacrifice
Jul-90	Partners In Kryme	Turtle Power
Jul-90	Bombalurina	Itsy Bitsy Teeny Weeny Yellow Polka Dot Bikini
Aug-90	Steve Miller Band	The Joker
Sep-90	Maria McKee	Show Me Heaven
Oct-90	Beautiful South	A Little Time
Oct-90	Righteous Brothers	Unchained Melody
Nov-90	Vanilla Ice	Ice Ice Baby
Dec-90	Cliff Richard	Saviour's Day
Dec-90	Enigma	Sadness Part 1
Jan-91	Iron Maiden	Bring Your Daughter... To The Slaughter

Jan-91	KLF feat. The Children of The Revolution	3AM Eternal
Jan-91	Simpsons	Do The Bartman
Jan-91	Queen	Innuendo
Feb-91	Chesney Hawkes	The One And Only
Mar-91	Clash	Should I Stay Or Should I Go
Mar-91	Hale & Pace & The Stonkers	The Stonk
Apr-91	Cher	The Shoop Shoop Song (It's In His Kiss)
May-91	Color Me Badd	I Wanna Sex You Up
Jun-91	Jason Donovan	Any Dream Will Do
Jun-91	Bryan Adams	(Everything I Do) I Do It For You
Oct-91	Vic Reeves & The Wonder Stuff	Dizzy
Nov-91	U2	The Fly
Nov-91	Michael Jackson	Black Or White
Dec-91	George Michael with Elton John	Don't Let The Sun Go Down On Me
Dec-91	Queen	Bohemian Rhapsody
Jan-92	Wet Wet Wet	Goodnight Girl
Jan-92	Shakespears Sister	Stay
Mar-92	Right Said Fred	Deeply Dippy
Apr-92	KWS	Please Don't Go / Game Boy
Jun-92	Erasure	Abba-Esque EP
Jul-92	Snap	Rhythm Is A Dancer
Jul-92	Jimmy Nail	Ain't No Doubt
Sep-92	Shamen	Ebeneezer Goode
Sep-92	Boyz II Men	End Of The Road
Sep-92	Tasmin Archer	Sleeping Satellite
Oct-92	Charles & Eddie	Would I Lie To You
Nov-92	Whitney Houston	I Will Always Love You
Jan-93	2 Unlimited	No Limit
Feb-93	Shaggy	Oh Carolina
Mar-93	Bluebells	Young At Heart (re-issue)
May-93	George Michael & Queen with Lisa Stansfield	Five Live EP

May-93	Ace Of Base	All That She Wants
May-93	UB40	(I Can't Help) Falling In Love With You
Jun-93	Gabrielle	Dreams
Jul-93	Take That	Pray
Jul-93	Freddie Mercury	Living On My Own
Aug-93	Culture Beat	Mr Vain
Sep-93	Jazzy Jeff & The Fresh Prince	Boom! Shake The Room
Oct-93	Meat Loaf	I'd Do Anything For Love (But I Won't Do That)
Oct-93	Take That featuring Lulu	ReLight My Fire
Dec-93	Mr Blobby	Mr Blobby
Dec-93	Take That	Babe
Dec-93	Chaka Demus & Pliers	Twist And Shout
Jan-94	D:Ream	Things Can Only Get Better
Feb-94	Mariah Carey	Without You
Mar-94	Doop	Doop
Apr-94	Take That	Everything Changes
Apr-94	Artist Formerly Known As Prince	The Most Beautiful Girl In The World
Apr-94	Tony Di Bart	The Real Thing
Apr-94	Manchester United Football Club	Come On You Reds
May-94	Stiltskin	Inside
May-94	Wet Wet Wet	Love Is All Around
Sep-94	Whigfield	Saturday Night
Oct-94	Pato Banton	Baby Come Back
Oct-94	Take That	Sure
Oct-94	Celine Dion	Think Twice
Nov-94	Baby D	Let Me Be Your Fantasy
Dec-94	East 17	Stay Another Day
Dec-94	Rednex	Cotton Eye Joe
Mar-95	Outhere Brothers	Don't Stop
Mar-95	Cher, Chrissie Hynde & Neneh Cherry with Eric Clapton	Love Can Build A Bridge
Apr-95	Take That	Back For Good
May-95	Oasis	Some Might Say

May-95	Livin' Joy	Dreamer (remix)
May-95	Robson & Jerome	Unchained Melody / The White Cliffs Of Dover
Jun-95	Outhere Brothers	Boom Boom Boom
Aug-95	Take That	Never Forget
Aug-95	Blur	Country House
Sep-95	Michael Jackson	You Are Not Alone
Sep-95	Shaggy	Boombastic
Sep-95	Simply Red	Fairground
Oct-95	Coolio featuring LV	Gangsta's Paradise
Nov-95	Robson & Jerome	I Believe / Up On The Roof
Dec-95	Michael Jackson	Earth Song
Jan-96	George Michael	Jesus To A Child
Jan-96	Babylon Zoo	Spaceman
Mar-96	Oasis	Don't Look Back In Anger
Mar-96	Take That	How Deep Is Your Love
Mar-96	Mark Morrison	Return Of The Mack
Mar-96	Prodigy	Firestarter
Apr-96	Gina G	Ooh Aah... Just A Little Bit
May-96	George Michael	Fast Love
Jun-96	Baddiel & Skinner and The Lightning Seeds	3 Lions
Jun-96	Fugees	Killing Me Softly
Jul-96	Gary Barlow	Forever Love
Jul-96	Spice Girls	Wannabe
Sep-96	Peter Andre	Flava
Sep-96	Fugees	Ready Or Not
Sep-96	Deep Blue Something	Breakfast At Tiffany's
Oct-96	Chemical Brothers	Setting Sun
Oct-96	Boyzone	Words
Oct-96	Spice Girls	Say You'll Be There
Nov-96	Robson & Jerome	What Becomes Of The Broken Hearted
Nov-96	Prodigy	Breathe
Dec-96	Peter Andre	I Feel You
Dec-96	Boyzone	A Different Beat
Dec-96	Dunblane	Knockin On Heaven's Door / Throw These Guns Away

Name that Song!

Dec-96	Spice Girls	2 Become 1
Jan-97	Tori Amos	Professional Widow
Jan-97	White Town	Your Woman
Feb-97	Blur	Beetlebum
Feb-97	LL Cool J	Ain't Nobody
Feb-97	U2	Discotheque
Feb-97	No Doubt	Don't Speak
Mar-97	Spice Girls	Mama / Who Do You Think You Are
Mar-97	R Kelly	I Believe I Can Fly
Apr-97	Chemical Brothers	Block Rockin' Beats
May-97	Michael Jackson	Blood On The Dancefloor
May-97	Gary Barlow	Love Won't Wait
May-97	Olive	You're Not Alone
May-97	Eternal featuring BeBe Winans	I Wanna Be The Only One
Jun-97	Hanson	Mmmbop
Jun-97	Puff Daddy & Faith Evans (featuring 112)	I'll Be Missing You
Jul-97	Oasis	D'You Know What I Mean?
Aug-97	Will Smith	Men In Black
Sep-97	Verve	The Drugs Don't Work
Sep-97	Elton John	Candle In The Wind 97
Oct-97	Aqua	Barbie Girl
Oct-97	Spice Girls	Spice Up Your Life
Nov-97	All Saints	Never Ever
Nov-97	Various Artists	Perfect Day
Dec-97	Teletubbies	Teletubbies Say Eh-Oh!
Dec-97	Spice Girls	Too Much
Jan-98	Oasis	All Around The World
Jan-98	Usher	You make Me Wanna
Feb-98	Aqua	Doctor Jones
Feb-98	Celine Dion	My Heart Will Go On
Feb-98	Cornershop	Brimful Of Asha
Mar-98	Madonna	Frozen
Mar-98	Run DMC vs Jason Nevins	It's Like That
Apr-98	Tamperer featuring Maya	Feel It
May-98	Boyzone	All That I Need
May-98	All Saints	Under The Bridge / Lady

		Marmalade
May-98	Aqua	Turn Back Time
Jun-98	B*Witched	C'est La Vie
Jun-98	Baddiel & Skinner and The Lightning Seeds	3 Lions '98
Jul-98	Billie	Because We Want To
Jul-98	Another Level	Freak Me
Jul-98	Jamiroquai	Deeper Underground
Aug-98	Spice Girls	Viva Forever
Aug-98	Boyzone	No Matter What
Sep-98	Manic Street Preachers	If You Tolerate This Your Children Will Be Next
Sep-98	All Saints	Bootie Call
Sep-98	Robbie Williams	Millennium
Sep-98	Melanie B feat Missy 'Misdemeanor' Elliott	I Want You Back
Oct-98	B*Witched	Rollercoaster
Oct-98	Billie	Girlfriend
Oct-98	Spacedust	Gym And Tonic
Oct-98	Cher	Believe
Nov-98	Steps	Heartbeat / Tragedy
Dec-98	B*Witched	To You I Belong
Dec-98	Chef	Chocolate Salty Balls
Dec-98	Spice Girls	Goodbye
Jan-99	Fatboy Slim	Praise You
Jan-99	911	A Little Bit More
Jan-99	Offspring	Pretty Fly (For A White Guy)
Feb-99	Armand Van Helden	You Don't Know Me
Feb-99	Blondie	Maria
Feb-99	Lenny Kravitz	Fly Away
Feb-99	Britney Spears	Baby One More Time
Mar-99	Boyzone	When The Going Gets Tough
Mar-99	B*Witched	Blame It On The Weatherman
Apr-99	Mr Oizo	Flat Beat
Apr-99	Martine McCutcheon	Perfect Moment
May-99	Westlife	Swear It Again
May-99	Backstreet Boys	I Want It That Way

May-99	Boyzone	You Needed Me
May-99	Shanks & Bigfoot	Sweet Like Chocolate
Jun-99	Baz Luhrmann	Everybody's Free (To Wear Sunscreen)
Jun-99	S Club 7	Bring It All Back
Jun-99	Vengaboys	Boom Boom Boom Boom
Jul-99	ATB	9pm (Till I Come)
Jul-99	Ricky Martin	Livin' La Vida Loca
Aug-99	Ronan Keating	When You Say Nothing At All
Aug-99	Westlife	If I Let You Go
Aug-99	Geri Halliwell	Mi Chico Latino
Sep-99	Lou Bega	Mambo No 5 (A Little Bit Of ...)
Sep-99	Vengaboys	We're Going To Ibiza!
Sep-99	Eiffel 65	Blue (Da Ba Dee)
Oct-99	Christina Aguilera	Genie In A Bottle
Oct-99	Westlife	Flying Without Wings
Nov-99	Five	Keep On Movin'
Nov-99	Geri Halliwell	Lift Me Up
Nov-99	Robbie Williams	She's The One / It's Only Us
Nov-99	Wamdue Project	King Of My Castle
Nov-99	Cliff Richard	The Millennium Prayer
Dec-99	Westlife	I Have A Dream / Seasons In The Sun
Jan-00	Manic Street Preachers	The Masses Against The Classes
Jan-00	Britney Spears	Born To Make You Happy
Feb-00	Gabrielle	Rise
Feb-00	Oasis	Go Let It Out
Feb-00	All Saints	Pure Shores
Mar-00	Madonna	American Pie
Mar-00	Chicane featuring Bryan Adams	Don't Give Up
Mar-00	Geri Halliwell	Bag It Up
Apr-00	Melanie C featuring Lisa Left Eye Lopes	Never Be The Same Again
Apr-00	Westlife	Fool Again
Apr-00	Craig David	Fill Me In
Apr-00	Fragma	Toca's Miracle

Create Your Own Pop-Pickers Quiz

Date	Artist	Title
May-00	Oxide & Neutrino	Bound 4 Da Reload (Casualty)
May-00	Britney Spears	Oops!... I Did It Again
May-00	Madison Avenue	Don't Call Me Baby
May-00	Billie Piper	Day And Night
Jun-00	Sonique	It Feels So Good
Jun-00	Black Legend	You See The Trouble With Me
Jul-00	Kylie Minogue	Spinning Around
Jul-00	Eminem	The Real Slim Shady
Jul-00	Corrs	Breathless
Jul-00	Ronan Keating	Life is A Rollercoaster
Jul-00	Five & Queen	We Will Rock You
Aug-00	Craig David	7 Days
Aug-00	Robbie Williams	Rock DJ
Aug-00	Melanie C	I Turn To You
Aug-00	Spiller	Groovejet (If This Ain't Love)
Sep-00	Madonna	Music
Sep-00	A1	Take On Me
Sep-00	Modjo	Lady (Hear Me Tonight)
Sep-00	Mariah Carey & Westlife	Against All Odds
Oct-00	All Saints	Black Coffee
Oct-00	U2	Beautiful Day
Oct-00	Steps	Stomp
Nov-00	Spice Girls	Holler / Let Love Lead The Way
Nov-00	Westlife	My Love
Nov-00	A1	Same Old Brand New You
Nov-00	LeAnn Rimes	Can't Fight The Moonlight
Dec-00	Destiny's Child	Independent Women Part 1
Dec-00	S Club 7	Never Had A Dream Come True
Dec-00	Bob The Builder	Can We Fix It?
Dec-00	Eminem	Stan
Jan-01	Rui Da Silva featuring Cassandra	Touch Me
Jan-01	Jennifer Lopez	Love Don't Cost A Thing
Jan-01	Limp Bizkit	Rollin'
Feb-01	Atomic Kitten	Whole Again

189

Mar-01	Shaggy featuring Rikrok	It Wasn't Me
Mar-01	Westlife	Uptown Girl
Mar-01	Hear'Say	Pure And Simple
Apr-01	Emma Bunton	What Took You So Long
Apr-01	Destiny's Child	Survivor
May-01	S Club 7	Don't Stop Movin'
May-01	Geri Halliwell	It's Raining Men
Jun-01	DJ Pied Piper & The Master Of Ceremonies	Do You Really Like It
Jun-01	Shaggy featuring Rayvon	Angel
Jun-01	Christina Aguilera, Lil' Kim, Mya & Pink	Lady Marmalade
Jul-01	Hear'Say	The Way To Your Love
Jul-01	Roger Sanchez	Another Chance
Jul-01	Robbie Williams	Eternity / The Road To Mandalay
Aug-01	Atomic Kitten	Eternal Flame
Aug-01	So Solid Crew	21 Seconds
Aug-01	Five	Let's Dance
Sep-01	Blue	Too Close
Sep-01	Bob The Builder	Mambo No 5
Sep-01	DJ Otzi	Hey Baby (Uuh, Aah)
Sep-01	Kylie Minogue	Can't Get You Out Of My Head
Oct-01	Afroman	Because I Got High
Nov-01	Westlife	Queen Of My Heart
Nov-01	Blue	If You Come Back
Dec-01	S Club 7	Have You Ever
Dec-01	Daniel Bedingfield	Gotta Get Thru This
Dec-01	Robbie Williams & Nicole Kidman	Somethin' Stupid
Jan-02	Aaliyah	More Than A Woman
Jan-02	George Harrison	My Sweet Lord
Feb-02	Enrique Iglesias	Hero
Mar-02	Westlife	World Of Our Own
Mar-02	Will Young	Anything Is Possible / Evergreen
Mar-02	Gareth Gates	Unchained Melody
Apr-02	Oasis	The Hindu Times
May-02	Sugababes	Freak Like Me
May-02	Holly Valance	Kiss Kiss

May-02	Ronan Keating	If Tomorrow Never Comes
May-02	Liberty X	Just A Little
Jun-02	Eminem	Without Me
Jun-02	Will Young	Light My Fire
Jun-02	Elvis vs JXL	A Little Less Conversation
Jul-02	Gareth Gates	Anyone Of Us (Stupid Mistake)
Aug-02	Darius	Colourblind
Aug-02	Sugababes	Round Round
Aug-02	Blazin' Squad	Crossroads
Sep-02	Atomic Kitten	The Tide Is High (Get The Feeling)
Sep-02	Pink	Just Like A Pill
Oct-02	Will Young & Gareth Gates	The Long And Winding Road / Suspicious Minds
Oct-02	Las Ketchup	The Ketchup Song (Asereje)
Oct-02	Nelly featuring Kelly Rowland	Dilemma
Nov-02	DJ Sammy & Yanou featuring Do	Heaven
Nov-02	Westlife	Unbreakable
Nov-02	Christina Aguilera featuring Redman	Dirrty
Dec-02	Daniel Bedingfield	If You're Not The One
Dec-02	Eminem	Lose Yourself
Dec-02	Blue featuring Elton John	Sorry Seems To Be The Hardest Word
Dec-02	Girls Aloud	Sound Of The Underground
Jan-03	David Sneddon	Stop Living The Lie
Feb-03	Tatu	All The Things She Said
Mar-03	Christina Aguilera	Beautiful
Mar-03	Gareth Gates featuring The Kumars	Spirit In The Sky
Apr-03	Room 5 featuring Oliver Cheatham	Make Luv
May-03	Busted	You Said No
May-03	Tomcraft	Loneliness

May-03	R Kelly	Ignition Remix
Jun-03	Evanescence	Bring Me To Life
Jul-03	Beyonce	Crazy In Love
Aug-03	Daniel Bedingfield	Never Gonna Leave Your Side
Aug-03	Blu Cantrell featuring Sean Paul	Breathe
Sep-03	Elton John	Are You Ready For Love
Sep-03	Black Eyed Peas	Where Is The Love
Oct-03	Sugababes	Hole In The Head
Nov-03	Fatman Scoop featuring The Crooklyn Clan	Be Faithful
Nov-03	Kylie Minogue	Slow
Nov-03	Busted	Crashed The Wedding
Nov-03	Westlife	Mandy
Dec-03	Will Young	Leave Right Now
Dec-03	Ozzy & Kelly Osbourne	Changes
Dec-03	Michael Andrews featuring Gary Jules	Mad World
Jan-04	Michelle	All This Time
Feb-04	LMC vs U2	Take Me To The Clouds Above
Feb-04	Sam & Mark	With A Little Help From My Friends / Measure Of A Man
Feb-04	Busted	Who's David?
Mar-04	Peter Andre	Mysterious Girl (re-issue)
Mar-04	Britney Spears	Toxic
Mar-04	DJ Casper	Cha Cha Slide
Mar-04	Usher featuring Lil' Jon & Ludacris	Yeah
Apr-04	McFly	Five Colours In Her Hair
Apr-04	Eamon	F**k It (I Don't Want You Back)
May-04	Frankee	F.U.R.B. (F U Right Back)
Jun-04	Mario Winans featuring Enya & P Diddy	I Don't Wanna Know
Jun-04	Britney Spears	Everytime
Jul-04	McFly	Obviously